WHAT THE BUTLER SAW

Joe Orton was born in Leicester in 1933 and died in August 1967. He left school at sixteen and two years later went to the Royal Academy of Dramatic Art. His first play to be staged, *Entertaining Mr. Sloane*, won the London Critics' "Variety" Award as the best play of 1964. *Loot*, his second play to be staged, won the *Evening Standard* Drama Award for the best play of 1966. *The Ruffian on the Stair* and *The Erpingham Camp* were performed as a double bill at the Royal Court Theatre in June 1967 under the title *Crimes of Passion*. His television plays, *The Good and Faithful Servant* and *Funeral Games*, were shown in 1967 and 1968. *What the Butler Saw*, his last play, was staged in 1969.

*Other books by Joe Orton
published by Grove Press*

ENTERTAINING MR. SLOANE
LOOT

Joe Orton

WHAT THE BUTLER SAW

Introduction by
John Lahr

GROVE PRESS, INC.
NEW YORK

First published by Methuen & Co Ltd, 1969
"Artist of the Outrageous" first appeared in *Evergreen Review*

Library of Congress Catalog Card Number: 78-139263

First Evergreen Edition, 1970
First Printing

Manufactured in the United States of America

Artist of
The Outrageous

by John Lahr

PRENTICE: I'm a rationalist.
RANCE: You can't be a rationalist in an irrational world.
It isn't rational.

Joe Orton,
What the Butler Saw

With madness, as with vomit, it's the passer-by who
receives the inconvenience . . .   Joe Orton,
The Erpingham Camp

Joe Orton was the comedian of the dark side of the contemporary soul: the vituperative anti-Christ, isolated by his
anarchist rage and cynical in his desolation. At the age of
thirty-four, Orton was bludgeoned to death in his sleep by his
roommate. This macabre demise is the kind of madness Orton
savored in his farces. Bloody, perverse, ostensibly motiveless –
Orton's murder would have seemed to him the final outrage: a
death as mysterious, gratuitous, and amoral as his birth.

Orton gives a logic and an emotional truth to the perverse in
experience. In his early plays – *The Ruffian on the Stair* (1964),
Entertaining Mr. Sloane (1964) – the outrageous springs from
an apparent realism. Society's mores are always butting heads
with fatuous catastrophe. (As one prissy onlooker observes in
the bedlam of Orton's *What the Butler Saw:* "Two young
people – one mad and one sexually insatiable – both naked –
are roaming this house. At all costs we must prevent a collision.") In Orton's plays, madness and reason inevitably
collide. There is a humanity behind this, an attempt to make

v

an audience learn from its outcasts and understand that every man is lost, bound together in communal madness. Orton tries to establish through theater the new channels of feeling R. D. Laing has postulated in psychology:

> ... When will the charade turn to carnival? Saints may still be kissing lepers. It is high time lepers kissed the saints. ...[1]

Orton's plays offend in order to instruct and heal; they shatter the easy divisions of We and They, the good and the bad, the just and the unjust.

> INTERVIEWER: It's interesting how in *Loot* a number of people are offended in that so much of the action is centered around a coffin.
>
> ORTON: I never understand why, because if you're absolutely practical – and I hope I am – a coffin is only a box. One calls it a coffin and once you've called it a coffin it immediately has all sorts of implications. In *Entertaining Mr. Sloane* I wrote about a man who was interested in boys and liked having sex with boys. I wanted him to be played as if he was the most ordinary man in the world, and not as if the moment you wanted sex with boys you had to put on earrings and scent. This is very bad. ... It's compartmentalization again. Audiences love it, of course, because they're safe. ... What I wanted to do in *Sloane* was break down all the sexual compartments people have. ...[2]

Orton's wit exposes the arrogance behind conventional wisdom. In *The Erpingham Camp* (1967), a priest initiates an eager new flunky at a holiday resort into the corporate structure. He hands the young man a Bible: "Take God's blessing with you, my son. And remember always to keep the little book I gave you. The words are obscure but the pictures will keep you

---

[1] R. D. Laing, *The Politics of Experience* (New York: Pantheon Books, 1967), p. 67.

[2] "Joe Orton Interviewed by Giles Gordon," *Transatlantic Review* #24, pp. 93-100.

from harm." Orton preys on those institutions which enforce a pious authority and an emotional rigidity: the Church ("It's life that defeats the Christian Church. She's always been able to deal with death"), the State ("You're at liberty to answer your own doorbell, miss. That is how we tell whether or not we live in a free country").

The outrageous can become shrill and extreme in its hate; but Orton's humor is deliciously double-edged in skewering both victim and victimizer. Orton denies synthetic emotions. In *The Ruffian on the Stair*, Mike, a petty thief, lives with Joyce, a whore who is his "wife." An intruder, Wilson, seeks revenge for the hit-and-run killing of his brother. Mike shoots Wilson, ostensibly for "sleeping" with Joyce. A stray bullet breaks the goldfish bowl.

> JOYCE: They're dead. Poor things. And I reared them so carefully. And while all this was going on they died.
> MIKE: Sit down. I'll fetch the police. This has been a crime of passion. They'll understand. They have wives and goldfish of their own.
>
> (JOYCE *is too heartbroken to answer. She buries her face in Mike's shoulder. He holds her close. Curtain.*)

Orton's couple are left in squalid yet hilarious isolation. The value of human life is less than that of a goldfish. Orton's objectivity will not allow sentimentality even among the most intimate social rituals like a funeral. In *Loot* (1966), the son of the deceased refuses the ex-nurse's suggestion to pay his respects to the dead.

> FAY: What excuse do you give?
> HAL: It would upset me.
> FAY: That's exactly what a funeral is meant to do.

From Orton's perspective, the outrageous is in the eyes of the beholder. In *Loot*, Hal, the homosexual son, contemplates burying his mother nude in order to put his stolen money in her coffin, and plots with the ex-nurse about how she'll marry his father to get the inheritance:

HAL: Bury her naked? My own Mum? (*He goes to the mirror and combs his hair.*) It's a Freudian nightmare.

DENNIS: I won't disagree.

HAL: Aren't we committing some kind of unforgivable sin?

DENNIS: Only if you're Catholic

In Orton's plays, sexuality is as ordinary as mashed potatoes. Hal admits his predilection for boys; the nurse scolds him:

FAY: Most people of any influence will ignore you. You'll be forced to associate with young men like yourself. Does that prospect please you?

HAL: I'm not sure.

FAY: Well, hesitation is something to be going on with. We can build on that. What will you do when you're old?

HAL: I shall die.

FAY: I see you're determined to run the gamut of all experience.

Sexual appetite is its own justification. In *Entertaining Mr. Sloane*, a brother and sister both have sexual designs on a boarder, Sloane, who proceeds to kill their father. They decide, finally, to share him for their pleasure rather than turn him over to the police. Ed and Kath argue over him with the righteousness of conventional indignation:

KATH: I gave him everything. . . . What more could he want?

ED: Freedom.

KATH: He's free with me.

ED: You're immoral.

KATH: He's clean living by nature; that's every man's right.

Orton disguises himself as an immoralist in order to re-examine the morality of the age. Orton's outrageousness works against conventional response. He puts his anger within a theatrical structure whose framework gives the stage actions humor as well as menace. The melodramatic conventions of

modern "serious theater" (and their implications) become his
targets as well as his dramatic devices. The Intruder and the
Unknown are part of a melodramatic pattern whose comfort-
able tension Orton inverts. In *The Ruffian on the Stair*, the
"villain," Wilson, enters an emotional wasteland instead of a
bower of domestic tranquillity. He is neither a frothing imbe-
cile nor a chest-thumping rapist. He has, in fact, an eye for the
men:

> I'm a Gent's hairdresser. Qualified. My dad has a business.
> Just a couple of chairs. I've clipped some notable heads
> in my time. Mostly professional men. Though we had an
> amateur street musician in a few weeks ago. We gave him
> satisfaction, I believe.

When Wilson is gunned down, Orton uses the moment to
mock the tidy emotional clarity of melodrama. Instead of the
status quo being restored, ignorance is compounded:

> WILSON: He's shot me. My will is in my overcoat pocket.
>   My address in my pocket diary. Remember, will you?
> JOYCE (*to* MIKE): What've you done?
> WILSON: He took it serious. How charming. (*He coughs,
>   blood spurts from his mouth.*) He's a bit of a nutter if you
>   ask me. Am I dying? I think . . . oh . . .
> JOYCE: He's fainted.

Death clarifies nothing. In the excess of stage emotion, there
need not be dignity. The gush of blood from Wilson's mouth
impresses Joyce only enough to make her venture that he has
passed out. The brutality of life, in Orton's eyes, comes from
mankind's unwillingness to see what it has created. The outrageous is a means of denying this process of evasion. At the
conclusion of *Loot*, with the money safe, the nurse, the son,
and his boyfriend happily free of the law, Orton concludes with
a joke on the forced, bland harmony of conventional farce:

> HAL (*to* DENNIS): You can kip here, baby. Plenty of room
>   now. Bring your bags over tonight.
> FAY: When Dennis and I are married we'd have to move
>   out.

HAL: Why?

FAY: People would talk. We must keep up appearances.
(*Curtain.*)

The conclusions of boulevard farce are illusions which hide a
more disturbing truth. Orton's farces rejuvenate techniques of
melodrama within farce while commenting on them. In *What
the Butler Saw*, the psychiatrist inspector, Dr Rance, tries to
explain the situation to the wife of a resident psychiatrist:

RANCE: ... Your husband has made away with his
secretary!

MRS PRENTICE: Isn't that a little melodramatic, doctor?

RANCE: Lunatics are melodramatic. ...

By extending the complexities of plot and psychological re-
versals to the extremes of farce, Orton finds a theatrical format
whose size and tone match the pseudo-sanity he wants to
expose.

II

JOYCE: ... The number of humiliating admissions I've
made. You'd think it would draw me closer to some-
body. But it doesn't.   Joe Orton,
The Ruffian on the Stair

Farce is thought of as a bourgeois fun machine in which the
people of the stage world try frantically (and hopelessly) to
make connections with one another. The frenetic rhythms of
farce, the confusion of identity, and the passionate actions based
on misunderstanding offer a precise theatrical correlative to
Orton's view of social insanity. In farce, people are pushed out
of their minds, propelled by the momentum of circumstances,
not free will. As the impetus increases, humanity disintegrates
before our eyes. People bounce off one another, only to re-
bound in their stupor and try again. They speak in earnest;
but their private despair is swept away by the accumulation of
events. The farce structure, once so patently artificial, captures

the tempo and confusion of modern living. As R. D. Laing
points out:

> When the ultimate basis of our world is in question, we
> run to different holes in the ground, we scurry into roles,
> statuses, identities, interpersonal relations. . . . Each
> sometimes sees the same fragment of the whole situation
> differently; often our concern is with different presenta-
> tions of the original catastrophe.[3]

Boulevard farce takes place amid velour curtains and *chaise
longues*. It is a confident form, glorifying in the world's solidity.
Boulevard farce wears a debonair smile, is wordly-wise and
indifferent to the vagaries of the universe. Its laughter does not
acknowledge pain, only a world of jaded wealth, sweaty *affaires*,
passions conceived in boredom, and a fascination with the
gadgets and games of the *nouveaux riches*. No matter how tortu-
ous the convolutions of plot, the people in boulevard farce
manage to escape destruction. They are a little embarrassed
perhaps or momentarily foiled but never vanquished by their
ignorance. Boulevard farce underscores the middle-class day-
dream of coherence – a world where events have their order
and life's blows turn out to be benign.

Orton is a modern *farceur* who sees life as precarious. He
blasts the soft assumptions of boulevard entertainment while
mastering its mechanism for mayhem. Orton takes farce past
Feydeau. He moves the laughter out of the parlor and puts it in
a mortuary (*Loot*) and a psychiatric clinic (*What the Butler
Saw*). The predicaments of the old farce (the secret rendezvous,
the hidden lover, the foolproof plan) have the potential, but not
the conviction, of tragedy. In Orton's farces, the only destiny
is an ambiguous survival.

Orton brings farce back to the world of death, destruction,
and betrayal that boulevard laughter tries to gloss over in its
confidence. Orton's humor confronts life instead of escaping
from it. Where Feydeau avoids higher seriousness in his fun,

---

[3] Laing, *op. cit.*, p. 74.

Orton finds a despair in laughter which chronicles the psychic death in life. Orton's world offers no safety to its characters, only violent adjustments – as random and urgent as the predicaments of farce. At the end of *Loot*, the police inspector arrests the wrong man: Mr McLeavy, the recent widower and father of the robber. As McLeavy is carted off to jail, he screams a testimony. His righteous indignation confuses morality with Catholic superstition. He exits saying: "I'm innocent. I'm innocent. Oh, what a terrible thing to happen to a man who's been kissed by the Pope."

Farce is the most anarchic stage form. Characters are motivated not by deep rational understanding or insight but by intuition and the vagaries of the moment. For Orton, nothing could be better suited to his purpose of demythologizing man's rational powers. In *Entertaining Mr. Sloane*, Sloane confesses that he killed a man: "I had no motive." In farce, this intellectual ambivalence is carried to outrageous extremes. It is the genre's power that the characters who vault out of closets or dash under beds at superhuman speeds do so in the name of the most primitive impulses. Most types of theater emphasize man's rationality; farce emphasizes his animality. *Loot* is Orton's first full-fledged farce. The play exudes a joyous literary liberation and a sense of control. It is as if – having found the form for his talent – Orton wanted to topple every boundary. At the funeral parlor, the deceased receives a memorial wreath from the Friends of Bingo! Fay, the nurse who at the age of twenty-eight, has already outlived and outwitted seven husbands, urges the widower, Mr. McLeavy, to marry her. "Go ahead," she says. "Ask me to marry you. I've no intention of refusing. On your knees. I'm a great believer in traditional positions." Unlike boulevard farce where the language is as mundane as the people, Orton's words are as unpredictable and unnerving as his characters' morality.

In farce, the body is transformed by anarchy's energy. Man no longer stands quite erect, but is changed by farce into a more acrobatic and contorted machine. The body undergoes the gamut of pulverizing experiences. In *Loot*, for instance, the son, Hal, dumps his mother's corpse in a closet to make room for the stolen money in the casket. The humiliation is compounded when they drag her out to undress her in order to do away with any evidence:

FAY: Are you committed to having her teeth removed?
HAL: Yes.... (*He holds up her teeth.*) ... These are good
  teeth. Are they the National Health?
FAY: No. She bought them out of her winnings. She had
  some good evenings at the table last year.

When they are transferring the body from the closet, an eye falls out. The culprits scramble on their hands and knees in search of it; not to preserve the wholeness of the corpse, but to eliminate the evidence. The detective, Truscott, discovers it; but, typical of Orton's vision of inhumanity, he has difficulty identifying the part of the human anatomy. The stage direction reads: "... *He holds it to the light in order to get a better view. Puzzled. He sniffs at it. He holds it close to his ear. He rattles it. He takes out a pocket magnifying glass and stares hard at it....*"

Whereas *Loot* and *The Erpingham Camp* explore farce as anarchy, *What the Butler Saw* (1969) extends the genre to a vision of total madness. Orton's most profound and most skillful play integrates his wit with masterful contortions of plot. *What the Butler Saw* builds an internal pressure and mental confusion which simulates the despair behind neurosis. Dr Prentice, a psychiatrist, is sneakily attempting to undress his new secretary under the ruse of a medical checkup. Enter Mrs Prentice, a nymphomaniac who loathes her husband. She confesses to being blackmailed by the page boy at a local hotel for previous indiscretions with him. Dr Prentice tries to hide his seminude secretary from his wife. The page boy arrives with photographs of Mrs Prentice in the act. He gets mixed up in the confusion. The girl must dress in his page-boy costume to escape. The boy must wear a wig and skirt to go unnoticed. Added to the hysteria of this scramble, the psychiatrist inspector, Dr Rance, comes to look over the clinic and arrives at the conclusion that Dr Prentice is sicker then anyone under his care.

This is the schizophrenic predicament as R. D. Laing has described it. Prentice too "does not know where he is or where he is going. He cannot get anywhere however hard he tries. . . . The future is the resultant of the present, the present is the resultant of the past and the past is unalterable."[4] Farce makes us forget everything but the manic needs of the moment. The audience sees the logic in Dr Prentice's cover-ups; the stage characters do not. He is not really mad; but the stage characters read madness into his every practical, private responses. This begins to erode his sense of sanity. Dr Prentice, for instance, writes letters to *The Guardian*. From this, his wife and Dr Rance deduce neurosis.

> MRS PRENTICE: Are you ashamed of the fact that you write to strange men?
>
> PRENTICE: There's nothing furtive in my relationship with the editor of *The Guardian*. . . .

All the characters in *What the Butler Saw* are numbed and dizzied by the speed of experience. They lose any sense of where and who they are. Mrs Prentice, a confessed nympho, sees her dream come true. The reality is too much. After witnessing the scurry of seminude bodies, she collapses, screaming: "Doctor, Doctor! The world is full of naked men running in all directions." Sexual identities are not only physically confused, but emotionally uncertain. Geraldine, the secretary dressed as a page boy, is interrogated by Dr Rance:

> RANCE: . . . Do you think yourself a girl?
>
> GERALDINE: No.
>
> RANCE: Why not?
>
> GERALDINE: I'm a boy.
>
> RANCE (*kindly*): Do you have the evidence about you?
>
> GERALDINE (*her eyes flashing an appeal to* DR PRENTICE): I must be a boy. I like girls.

---

[4] *Ibid.*, p. 79.

Events spiral out of control; each person sees them from his own angle. Farce never allows anyone on stage to see the same thing. This leads to a state of complete emotional polarization. Dr Prentice wants to commit Dr Rance, whose actions seem outrageous to *him;* and Dr Rance wants to commit Dr Prentice. There is no shared experience; each is struggling to preserve his sanity – not through understanding but by eliminating the source of tension:

> PRENTICE (*waving his gun*): . . . I'm going to certify you.
> RANCE (*quietly, with dignity*): No, I am going to certify you.
> PRENTICE: I have the weapon. You have the choice. What is it to be? Either madness or death?
> RANCE: Neither of your alternatives would enable me to continue to be employed by Her Majesty's Government.
> PRENTICE: That isn't true. The higher reaches of the civil service are recruited entirely from corpses or madmen. Press the Alarm!

Orton's image following this speech is stunning. When the alarm is pulled, grills come down over every door, and sirens sound. Caged, furious, and arrogant in its denial of madness, the stage world is so conscious of nightmare that the people in it can justifiably ask assurances of their existence. The page boy "crawls, almost faints" in a chair.

> NICK: What about me, sir? I'm not mad.
> RANCE (*with a smile*): You're not human.
> NICK: I can't be an hallucination. (*He points to his bleeding shoulder.*) Look at this wound. That's real.
> RANCE: It appears to be.
> NICK: If the pain is real I must be real.
> RANCE: I'd rather not get involved in metaphysical speculations.

III

There is a social truth behind farce's mechanics which connects the stage madness to the schizophrenic hysteria of contemporary life. Orton's genius is in making this connection. In farce, the characters become hilariously powerless in the face of events. Orton sees this not simply as the condition of fun, but of life. *What the Butler Saw* concludes with most of the characters stripped to their underwear by the vagaries of events. Their nakedness goes beyond humor to prophecy. "Let us put on our clothes and face the world," says Dr Rance. But in this modern evocation of Adam and the "fortunate fall," innocence, truth, and energy have been outlandishly betrayed. Orton's final stage direction leaves the audience with a devastating self-image: "*They pick up their clothes and weary, bleeding, drugged and drunk, climb the rope ladder into the blazing light.*"

Farce makes a shell game of experience: now you see it, now you don't. The audience is given an omniscience the characters never have. As the plot balloons, there is no way to control the confusions. The effect is to create a sense of powerlessness in the stage world which is at the root of neurosis in the real one. R. D. Laing has described the schizophrenic in terms that could apply to any Orton farce character:

> In his life situation the person comes to feel that he is in an untenable position. He cannot make a move, or make no move, without being beset by contradictory and paradoxical pressures and demands, pushes and pulls, both internally from himself and externally from those around him. He is, as it were, in a position of checkmate.[5]

Under these pressures man turns into himself as a tactic of evasion. He becomes mad to avoid the tensions of a mad and ruthless world. In *Loot*, the predicament is dramatized when Truscott arrests Mr McLeavy. The individual is trammeled by irresponsible authority:

MCLEAVY: I want to see someone in authority.
TRUSCOTT: I am an authority. You can see me.
MCLEAVY: Someone higher.

---

[5] *Loc. cit.*

TRUSCOTT: You can see whoever you like providing you convince me first that you're justified in seeing them.

The nightmare of this injustice is built into the logic of the system of farce, just as it is built into the system of government. Confusion, ignorance, and insanity reign under the disguise of propriety:

MCLEAVY: You're mad.
TRUSCOTT: Nonsense. I had a checkup only yesterday. Our medical officer assured me that I was quite sane.
MCLEAVY: I'm innocent. (*A little unsure of himself, the beginnings of panic.*) Doesn't that mean anything to you?

Orton shows how fragile the illusion of sanity is; and how, out of ignorance, people invoke their mental health. Mr McLeavy cannot make his case understood; Truscott parries his requests with words on a totally different moral wavelength. For McLeavy, the next step is madness. He knows the truth but is shown to be wrong by a man to whom truth and humanity have never mattered. McLeavy screams on stage out of fear of his impending powerlessness, just as Bobby Seale, bound and gagged in the Chicago Conspiracy trial, yelled to Judge Hoffman. Seale had dismissed his lawyer in order to defend himself. The lawyer, William Kunstler, had made this known to the judge; but the judge would not recognize the fact. The court dialogue has the painful truth of an Orton farce:

THE COURT: Mr. Seale and Mr. Kunstler, your lawyer, I must admonish you that such outbursts are considered by the Court to be contemptuous, contumacious, and will be dealt with appropriately in the future.
MR. KUNSTLER: Your Honor, the defendant was trying to defend himself, and I have already indicated my—
THE COURT: The defendant was not defending himself.
MR. SEALE: I was too defending myself. Any time anybody gives me the wrong symbol in the courtroom is deliberately—
THE COURT: He is not addressing me with authority—
MR. SEALE: —distorting and putting it on the record.

THE COURT: Instruct that man to keep quiet.

MR. SEALE: I want to defend myself. . . . No siree, I am not going to sit here and get that on the record. I am going to at least let it be known . . . that this man is erroneously representing symbols directly related to the party of which I am chairman.[6]

Orton's plays expose the method of social madness which America now experiences. The visible tension in farce has become the pattern of our society. As in Orton's plays, the nation has reached a momentum over Vietnam where truth no longer matters:

GERALDINE: I'm not a patient. I'm telling the truth.

RANCE: It's much too late to tell the truth.

Our political leaders, like Dr Rance in *What the Butler Saw*, are faced with their own brutality. Their evasion of this inhumanity is made in the name of "sanity" which they call pragmatism:

MRS PRENTICE: Is this real blood?

RANCE: No.

MRS PRENTICE: Can you see it?

RANCE: Yes.

MRS PRENTICE: Then what explanation is there?

RANCE: I'm a scientist. I state facts, I cannot be expected to provide explanations. Reject any para-normal phenomena. It's the only way to remain sane.

Spiro Agnew's impugning of the news media stems from the same psychotic impulse behind Dr Rance's words: the attempt to restore "sanity" by ignoring the madness which has been created in the name of reason. Agnew is talking the language of censorship under the guise of moral indignation. He does not want the truth of Vietnam or the protest movement to be *seen*. He forces those who protest against madness into a state of frustration approaching insanity. Ultimately, they must ask

---

6 Jason Epstein, "Bobby Seale's Trial," *New York Review of Books*, December 4, 1969, pp. 42-43.

what Orton's characters ask: are they real? Are the alternatives (Dr Prentice's words) madness or death? There seems to be no middle ground between what they know about the world and what the authority wants them to believe. This problem of perception is a theme reiterated through Orton's work and borne out in America. Agnew, in his famous Harrisburg, Pennyslvania, speech, welcomed this dichotomy. His words are as insane as Dr Rance's. He would feed the state of schizophrenia: " . . . If in challenging peace demonstrators we polarize American people, I say it is time for positive polarization." The protector willingly becomes the victimizer. Agnew speaks with a vague, intense patriotism. Like Detective Truscott in *Loot*, Agnew's words hide him from the violence of his actions. Truscott asks Hal where he has stashed the money. Hal answers. Then Truscott kicks him violently:

> TRUSCOTT: Don't lie to me!
> HAL: I'm not lying! It's in the church!
> TRUSCOTT (*shouting, knocking* HAL *to the floor*): Under any other political system I'd have you on the floor in tears.
> HAL (*crying*): You've got me on the floor in tears.

Repression is not merely a political maneuver; it is a psychotic response for dealing with the unknown. The paranoia of the right wing is fed by its ignorance of the world. Agnew talks of "separating the protest leaders from our society – with no more regret than we should feel over discarding rotten apples from a barrel." The same violent arrogance and pseudo-sanity is reflected in Dr Rance's righteous reaction to Dr Prentice's "crime." Like the Nixon Administration, Dr Rance has a barbaric conspiratorial view of the world which *sees things that do not exist yet cannot interpret the physical facts in front of it*:

> RANCE: . . . Society must be made aware of the growing menace of pornography. The whole treacherous avant-garde movement will be exposed for what it is – an instrument for inciting the humanity and the state. . . .

The velocity of public life has the momentum of an Orton farce. Like Orton's stage characters, the public is unwittingly numbed by the experience. "I've been too long among the mad to know what sanity is," confesses Dr Prentice, expressing a confusion of roles infecting our own society. President Nixon does not feel the shame of American massacres nor see the nation's mortifying defeats in Vietnam when he talks of our "destiny," or when he maintains: "North Vietnam cannot defeat or humiliate the United States." The madness lies in his inability to see what is happening to the country he leads as well as the one he would defend.

Orton's farces make an audience confront the schizophrenic patterns of their lives, rather than evade them. By making a carnival of man's stupidity and superstition, by exposing the condition of social insanity, his plays hold out to an audience the possibility of humility and care. As a genre, farce has a power and insidious appeal which is becoming more pertinent to our historical moment. Orton's plays, especially *What the Butler Saw*, pave a new way for playwrights to create dangerously with laughter in dangerous times. Orton's writing is a testament to what American society is just beginning to realize: reality is the ultimate outrage.

'Surely we're all mad people, and they
'Whom we think are, are not.'

– The Revenger's Tragedy

The first London performance of *What the Butler Saw* was given at the Queen's Theatre by Lewenstein-Delfont Productions Ltd and H. M. Tennent Ltd on 5th March 1969, with the following cast in order of appearance:

DR PRENTICE	Stanley Baxter
GERALDINE BARCLAY	Julia Foster
MRS PRENTICE	Coral Browne
NICHOLAS BECKETT	Hayward Morse
DR RANCE	Ralph Richardson
SERGEANT MATCH	Peter Bayliss

Directed by   Robert Chetwyn
Designed by   Hutchinson Scott

The first American performance of *What the Butler Saw* was given at the McAlpin Rooftop Theater, New York, May 4, 1970, by arrangement with Lewenstein-Delfont Productions Ltd and H. M. Tennent Ltd; produced by·Charles Woodward and Michael Kasdan, directed by Joseph Hardy, designed by William Ritman, costumes by Ann Roth, and with the following cast:

DR PRENTICE	Laurence Luckinbill
GERALDINE BARCLAY	Diana Davila
MRS PRENTICE	Jan Farrand
NICHOLAS BECKETT	Charlie Murphy
DR RANCE	Lucian Scott
SERGEANT MATCH	Tom Rosqui

Act One

A room in a private clinic. Morning.
Doors lead to the wards, the dispensary and the hall. French
windows open on to pleasant gardens and shrubberies.
Sink. Desk. Consulting couch with curtains.

DR PRENTICE *enters briskly.* GERALDINE BARCLAY *follows*
him. She carries a small cardboard box.

PRENTICE (*turning at the desk*). Take a seat. Is this your first
job?

GERALDINE (*sitting*). Yes, doctor.

DR PRENTICE *puts on a pair of spectacles, stares at her. He*
opens a drawer in the desk, takes out a notebook.

PRENTICE (*picking up a pencil*). I'm going to ask you a few
questions. (*He hands her a notebook and pencil.*) Write
them down. In English, please. (*He returns to his desk, sits,*
smiles.) Who was your father? Put that at the head of the
page.

GERALDINE *puts the cardboard box she is carrying to one side,*
crosses her legs, rests the notebook upon her knee and makes a
note.

And now the reply immediately underneath for quick
reference.

GERALDINE. I've no idea who my father was.

DR PRENTICE *is perturbed by her reply although he gives no*
evidence of this. He gives her a kindly smile.

PRENTICE. I'd better be frank, Miss Barclay. I can't employ
you if you're in any way miraculous. It would be contrary
to established practice. You did have a father?

GERALDINE. Oh, I'm sure I did. My mother was frugal in her habits, but she'd never economize unwisely.

PRENTICE. If you had a father why can't you produce him?

GERALDINE. He deserted my mother. Many years ago. She was the victim of an unpleasant attack.

PRENTICE (*shrewdly*). She was a nun?

GERALDINE. No. She was a chambermaid at the Station Hotel.

DR PRENTICE *frowns, takes off his spectacles and pinches the bridge of his nose.*

PRENTICE. Pass that large, leather-bound volume, will you? I must check your story. To safeguard my interests, you understand?

GERALDINE *lifts the book from the book case and takes it to* DR PRENTICE.

(*Consulting the index.*) The Station Hotel?

GERALDINE. Yes.

PRENTICE (*opening the book, running his finger down the page*). Ah, here we are! It's a building of small architectural merit built for some unknown purpose at the turn of the century. It was converted into a hotel by public subscription. (*He nods, wisely.*) I stayed there once myself as a young man. It has a reputation for luxury which baffles the most undemanding guest. (*He closes the book with a bang and pushes it to one side.*) Your story appears, in the main, to be correct. This admirable volume, of course, omits most of the details. But that is only to be expected in a publication of wide general usage. (*He puts on his spectacles.*) Make a note to the effect that your father is missing. Say nothing of the circumstances. It might influence my final decision.

GERALDINE *makes a jotting in her notebook.* DR PRENTICE *takes the leather-bound volume to the bookcase.*

PRENTICE. Is your mother alive? Or has she too unaccountably vanished? That is a trick question. Be careful – you could lose marks on your final scoring.

He returns to his desk and pours himself a whisky.

GERALDINE. I haven't seen my mother for many years. I was brought up by a Mrs Barclay. She died recently.

PRENTICE. From what cause?

GERALDINE. An explosion, due to a faulty gas-main, killed her outright and took the roof off the house.

PRENTICE. Have you applied for compensation?

GERALDINE. Just for the roof.

PRENTICE. Were there no other victims of the disaster?

GERALDINE. Yes. A recently erected statue of Sir Winston Churchill was so badly injured that the George medal has been talked of. Parts of the great man were actually found embedded in my step-mother.

PRENTICE. Which parts?

GERALDINE. I'm afraid I can't help you there. I was too upset to supervise the funeral arrangements. Or, indeed, to identify the body.

PRENTICE. Surely the Churchill family did that?

GERALDINE. Yes. They were most kind.

PRENTICE. You've had a unique experience. It's not everyone has their step-mother assassinated by the North Thames Gas Board.

He shakes his head, sharing the poor girl's sorrow.

Can I get you an aspirin?

GERALDINE. No, thank you, sir. I don't want to start taking drugs.

PRENTICE. Your caution does you credit, my dear. (*He smiles in a kindly fashion.*) Now, I have to ask a question which may cause you embarrassment. Please remember that I'm a doctor. (*Pause.*) What is your shorthand speed?

GERALDINE. I can manage twenty words a minute with ease, sir.

PRENTICE. And your typing speed?

GERALDINE. I haven't mastered the keyboard. My money ran out, you see.

DR PRENTICE *takes the notebook from her and puts it aside.*

PRENTICE. Perhaps you have other qualities which aren't immediately apparent. Lie on that couch.

GERALDINE. Why, doctor?

PRENTICE. Never ask questions. That is the first lesson a secretary must learn. (*He pulls aside the curtains on the couch.*) And kindly remove your stockings. I wish to see what effect your step-mother's death had upon your legs.

GERALDINE. Isn't this rather unusual, doctor?

PRENTICE. Have no fear, Miss Barclay. What I see upon the couch isn't a lovely and desirable girl. It's a sick mind in need of psychiatric treatment. The body is of no interest to a man of my stamp. A woman once threw herself at me. I needn't tell you that this is spoken in confidence. She was stark naked. She wished me to misbehave myself. And, d'you know, all I was conscious of was that she had a malformed navel? That's how much notice I take of women's bodies.

GERALDINE. Please forgive me, doctor. I wasn't meaning to suggest that your attentions were in any way improper.

She takes off her shoes and stockings and lies on the couch. DR PRENTICE *runs a hand along her legs and nods, sagely.*

PRENTICE. As I thought. You've a febrile condition of the calves. You're quite wise to have a check-up. (*He straightens and takes off his spectacles.*) Undress.

He turns to the desk and takes off his coat. GERALDINE *sits up alarmed.*

GERALDINE. I've never undressed in front of a man before.

PRENTICE. I shall take account of your inexperience in these matters.

He puts his spectacles on the desk and rolls back his cuffs.

GERALDINE. I couldn't allow a man to touch me while I was unclothed.

PRENTICE. I shall wear rubber gloves.

GERALDINE *is worried and makes no attempt to conceal her growing doubts.*

GERALDINE. How long would I have to remain undressed?

PRENTICE. If your reactions are normal you'll be back on your feet in next to no time.

GERALDINE. My headmistress made no mention of this in her booklet 'Hints to the School-leaver'.

PRENTICE. The chapter dealing with medical examinations may have been omitted from the text.

GERALDINE. But that would be ridiculous in a work intended only for use in schools!

PRENTICE. Your concern is well-founded, Miss Barclay. Our educational system needs thoroughly looking into. Speak to your headmistress at her next 'old girls' get-together'.

He turns to the sink and rinses his hands.

GERALDINE. I'd like another woman present. Is your wife available?

PRENTICE. Mrs Prentice is attending a more than usually lengthy meeting of her coven. She won't be back until this evening.

GERALDINE. I could wait until then.

PRENTICE. I haven't the patience, my dear. I've a natural tendency to rush things. I won't trouble you with the details of my private life till you're dressed.

He picks up a towel and dries his hands.

PRENTICE. Put your clothes on the chair provided.

GERALDINE *unzips and removes her dress.* DR PRENTICE *watches her. Pause. He puts the towel aside and puts on his spectacles.*

I must ask you not to mention this examination to my wife. I'm not doing it under the Health Scheme, you see. She'd

be sure to send in a bill. And that would be open to misunderstanding.

GERALDINE. What is Mrs Prentice like, doctor? I've heard so
many stories about her.

She puts her dress aside and stands in her panties and bra.

PRENTICE. My wife is a nymphomaniac. Consequently, like
the Holy Grail, she's ardently sought after by young men.
I married her for her money and, upon discovering her to be
penniless, I attempted to throttle her. She escaped my
murderous fury and I've had to live with her malice ever
since.

GERALDINE (*with a sigh*). Poor Dr Prentice. How trying it
must be for you. (*Climbing on to the couch.*) I wish there were
something I could do to cheer you up.

She pulls close the curtains. DR PRENTICE *puts on a white
surgical coat.*

PRENTICE. Well, my dear, if it'll give you any pleasure you
can test my new contraceptive device.

GERALDINE *looks over the curtain and smiles sweetly.*

GERALDINE (*throwing her panties and bra into a chair*). I'll be
delighted to help you in any way I can, doctor.

PRENTICE (*with an indulgent, superior smile*). Lie on the couch
with your hands behind your head and think of the closing
chapters of your favourite work of fiction. The rest may be
left to me.

GERALDINE *disappears behind the curtain.* DR PRENTICE
goes to the drawer in his desk. MRS PRENTICE *enters from the
hall. She is wearing a costly fur coat.*

MRS PRENTICE. Who are you talking to?

DR PRENTICE *is surprised and angry at his wife's unexpected
appearance.*

PRENTICE (*flushing, guilty*). I must ask you not to enter my consulting-room without warning. You're interrupting my studies.

MRS PRENTICE *stares about the room.*

MRS PRENTICE. There's no one here. Were you talking to yourself?

PRENTICE. I was dictating a message to Matron. She's worried by her inability to control her bladder.

MRS PRENTICE. Can urine be controlled by thinking of *Tess of the D'Urbevilles*?

PRENTICE. My theory is still in the planning stage. I'd rather not discuss it.

MRS PRENTICE *goes to the desk and pours herself a drink.*

PRENTICE. Why have you returned? You know I can't endure the torment of being in your company.

MRS PRENTICE. I arrived at my meeting to find the hall in an uproar. Helen Duncanon had declared herself to be in love with a man. And, as you know, the club is primarily for lesbians. I myself am exempt from the rule because you count as a woman. We expelled Helen and I spent the night at the Station Hotel. (*She swallows her drink.*)

NICHOLAS BECKETT *enters. He is a hotel page. He wears a page-boy's uniform.*

NICK (*to* MRS PRENTICE). If you'd care to check your baggage, madam. I'd like to return to my duties.

MRS PRENTICE (*to* DR PRENTICE). Cast your eye across my luggage, will you? Half of it has already been stolen by the hotel staff. (*She turns to the table and pours a drink.*) It's so difficult being a woman.

PRENTICE. Well, I'm sure you're the best judge of that.

He goes into the hall, disgruntled. MRS PRENTICE *puts ice in her drink and turns to* NICK, *a cold expression on her face.*

MRS PRENTICE. I'm not asking for my handbag back, or for the money you've stolen, but unless my dress and wig are returned I shall file a complaint with your employers. You have until lunchtime.

NICK. I've already sold the dress for a lump sum. I could get it back at a price. I've also found someone to take an option on the photographs.

MRS PRENTICE *stares*.

MRS PRENTICE. What photographs?

NICK. I had a camera concealed in the room.

MRS PRENTICE (*open-mouthed*). When I gave myself to you the contract didn't include cinematic rights.

NICK. I'd like a hundred quid for the negatives. You've got until lunchtime.

MRS PRENTICE. I shall complain to the manager.

NICK. It will do you no good. He took the photographs.

MRS PRENTICE. Oh, this is scandalous! I'm a married woman.

NICK. You didn't behave like a married woman last night.

MRS PRENTICE. I was upset. A lesbian friend of mine had just announced her engagement to a Member of Parliament.

NICK. You must be more careful in your choice of friends. I'd like to get out of the indecent photograph racket. It's so wearing on the nerves. Can you find me a worthwhile job? I had a hard boyhood.

MRS PRENTICE. What kind of job do you want?

NICK. I'm an expert typist. I was taught by a man in the printing trade.

MRS PRENTICE (*firmly*). I'm willing to pay for the photographs, but I can't possibly recommend your typing.

NICK. I want a hundred pounds and the post of secretary to your husband!

MRS PRENTICE. You put me in an impossible position.

NICK. No position is impossible when you're young and healthy.

MRS PRENTICE *turns to the desk. She pours herself a drink. Her hand trembles.* DR PRENTICE *enters from the hall. He carries an overnight case.* MRS PRENTICE *puts an empty whisky bottle aside and drops ice into her glass.*

PRENTICE (*to* NICK). She'll be sodden before long. (*He puts the case down.*)

NICK. Have you a family, sir?

PRENTICE. No. My wife said breast-feeding would spoil her shape. Though, from what I remember, it would've been improved by a little nibbling.

MRS PRENTICE *gives a nervy toss of her head and drinks whisky.*

PRENTICE. She's an example of in-breeding among the lobelia-growing classes. A failure in eugenics, combined with a taste for alcohol and sexual intercourse, makes it most undesirable for her to become a mother.

MRS PRENTICE (*quietly*). I hardly ever have sexual intercourse.

PRENTICE. You were born with your legs apart. They'll send you to the grave in a Y-shaped coffin.

MRS PRENTICE (*with a brittle laugh*). My trouble stems from your inadequacy as a lover! It's embarrassing. You must've learned your technique from a Christmas cracker. (*Her mouth twists into a sneer.*) Rejuvenation pills have no effect on you.

PRENTICE (*stuffily*). I never take pills.

MRS PRENTICE. You take them all the time during our love-making. The deafening sound of your chewing is the reason for my never having an orgasm.

DR PRENTICE *is stung by her remarks. He approaches closer.*

PRENTICE. How dare you say that! Your book on the climax in the female is largely autobiographical. (*Pause. He stares.*) Or have you been masquerading as a sexually responsive woman?

MRS PRENTICE. My uterine contractions have been bogus for some time!

She picks up her drink and triumphantly flounces into the ward carrying the overnight case.

PRENTICE (*looking after her*). What a discovery! Married to a mistress of the fraudulent climax. (*He pours himself a drink.*)

NICK (*after a pause*). My parents were divorced, sir. I missed the warmth of a happy family atmosphere.

PRENTICE. As a psychiatrist I do all I can to bring estranged couples together. (*He presses money into* NICK's *hand.*) Don't hesitate to call on me if you're mentally disturbed.

NICK *takes the money and goes into the hall.* DR PRENTICE, *drink in hand, pulls the curtain on the couch aside and looks through.*

PRENTICE. It's no good lying there, Miss Barclay. My wife has returned.

GERALDINE *looks over the curtain.*

GERALDINE. Oh, good! She'll be able to help with your examination.

PRENTICE. The examination is cancelled until further notice. (*He picks up the underclothes from the chair.*) Get dressed!

MRS PRENTICE *enters from the ward. She has an empty glass in her hand.*

MRS PRENTICE (*going to the desk*). Has your new secretary arrived?

DR PRENTICE *holds the underwear behind his back.* GERALDINE *is concealed by the curtain.*

PRENTICE. Yes. I've got her particulars somewhere.

Unable to conceal the underclothes behind his back, he drops them into a wastepaper basket. MRS PRENTICE *opens a new bottle of whisky.*

MRS PRENTICE. Have you ever given thought to a male secretary?

PRENTICE. A man could never get used to the work.

MRS PRENTICE. My father had a male secretary. My mother said he was much better than a woman.

PRENTICE. I couldn't ask a young fellow to do overtime and then palm him off with a lipstick or a bottle of Yardley's. It'd be silk suits and Alfa Romeos if I so much as breathed on him.

MRS PRENTICE. Try a boy for a change. You're a rich man. You can afford the luxuries of life.

PRENTICE. What will become of Miss Barclay? I've already given her a preliminary interview.

MRS PRENTICE. You must explain the altered circumstances.

GERALDINE *looks over the curtain.* DR PRENTICE *motions her down. She disappears. He picks up the shorthand pad, scribbles a note on it, and tosses it over the curtain.* MRS PRENTICE *pours herself a drink.* DR PRENTICE *sees Geraldine's dress lying on the chair and picks it up. He is about to drop it into the wastepaper basket with the underwear when* MRS PRENTICE *turns, drink in hand.* DR PRENTICE *attempts to conceal the dress behind his back. It hangs down.*

MRS PRENTICE (*in a surprised tone*). What are you doing with that dress?

PRENTICE (*pause*). It's an old one of yours.

MRS PRENTICE. Have you taken up transvestism? I'd no idea our marriage teetered on the edge of fashion.

PRENTICE. Our marriage is like the peace of God – it passeth all understanding.

MRS PRENTICE *swallows her drink and holds out her hand.*

MRS PRENTICE. Give me the dress. I shall wear it.

PRENTICE (*reluctant*). May I have the one you're wearing in exchange?

MRS PRENTICE (*putting glass down*). I'm not wearing a dress.

She slips off her fur coat. Under it she is dressed only in a slip.
DR PRENTICE *cannot conceal his surprise.*

PRENTICE. Why aren't you wearing a dress ? Are you following some extreme fashion ?

MRS PRENTICE (*putting on* GERALDINE's *dress*). I'm going to speak frankly and with complete candour. Please listen carefully and save your comments for later. (*She zips up the dress.*) My room at the hotel was small, airless and uncomfortable. A model of its kind. As I was dressing for dinner I noticed that the sheets on the bed were none too clean. I went to the linen cupboard, which I knew to be on the second floor, hoping to find a chambermaid. Instead I found a pageboy who enticed me into the cupboard and then made an indecent suggestion. When I repulsed him he attempted to rape me. I fought him off but not before he'd stolen my handbag and several articles of clothing.

PRENTICE. It doesn't sound the kind of behaviour one expects at a four-star hotel.

MRS PRENTICE. The boy has promised to return my dress. He's sold it to a friend who probably intends using it at sex orgies.

PRENTICE (*joining her at the desk*). Do you realize what would happen if your adventures became public ? I'd be ruined. The doors of London society would be slammed in my face. (*He pours a whisky.*) Did you inform the authorities of this escapade ?

MRS PRENTICE. No.

PRENTICE. Why not ?

MRS PRENTICE. I saw in his youth the remnants of a natural goodness that had all but been destroyed by the pressures of society. I promised to find him employment.

PRENTICE. Is there a market for illegal entrance ?

MRS PRENTICE. I don't propose to lead him into a dead-end job.

PRENTICE. What other qualifications has he ?

MRS PRENTICE. He can type.

PRENTICE. There aren't many jobs for male typists.

MRS PRENTICE. No. He's been depressed by his failure in commerce. That's why he took to rape.

PRENTICE. How do you hope to employ him?

MRS PRENTICE. As your secretary. He'll be back in an hour. You can check his credentials at your leisure. Where is Miss Barclay?

PRENTICE. She's upstairs.

MRS PRENTICE. I shall inform her that the situation is no longer vacant.

DR PRENTICE *swallows his drink and puts the glass down.*

PRENTICE. Could I borrow one of your dresses for a while, my dear?

MRS PRENTICE. I find your sudden craving for women's clothing a dull and, on the whole, a rather distasteful subject.

She puts her glass down and goes into the hall. DR PRENTICE *passes a hand across his brow.*

PRENTICE. She'll bring my grey hairs in sorrow to the grave. (*He goes to the couch, pulls curtain aside, and looks through.*) Miss Barclay – the present situation is fraught with danger – my wife is under the impression that your dress belongs to her.

GERALDINE *looks over the curtain.*

GERALDINE. We must explain, as tactfully as possible, that she has made a mistake.

PRENTICE. I'm afraid that is impossible. You must be patient for a little longer.

GERALDINE. Doctor – I'm naked! You do realize that, don't you?

PRENTICE (*a tremor passing across his face*). Indeed I do, Miss

Barclay. I'm sure it must cause you acute embarrassment.
I'll set about finding you suitable clothing.

*He turns to the wastepaper basket, and is about to remove the
underclothing when* DR RANCE *enters from the garden.* DR
PRENTICE *drops the clothing into the basket and puts the
basket down.* GERALDINE *ducks behind the curtain out of sight.*

RANCE (*with a polite smile*). Good morning. (*He takes off his
hat.*) Are you Dr Prentice?
PRENTICE. Yes. Have you an appointment?
RANCE. No. I never make appointments. (*He puts the hat and
the brief-case aside and shakes hands.*) I'd like to be given
details of your clinic. It's run, I understand, with the full
knowledge and permission of the local hospital authorities?
You specialize in the complete breakdown and its by-
products?
PRENTICE. Yes. But it's highly confidential. My files are never
open to strangers.
RANCE. You may speak freely in front of me. I represent Her
Majesty's Government. Your immediate superiors in madness. I'm from the Commissioners.
PRENTICE (*worried, taking off his spectacles*). Which branch?
RANCE. The mental branch.
PRENTICE. Do you cover asylums proper? Or just houses of
tentative madness?
RANCE. My brief is infinite. I'd have sway over a rabbit hutch
if the inmates were mentally disturbed. (*He opens the brief-
case, and takes out the notebook.*)

DR PRENTICE, *unsteadily, pours himself a whisky.*

PRENTICE. You're obviously a force to be reckoned with.
RANCE. I hope our relationship will be a pleasant one. Is this
your consulting-room?
PRENTICE (*swallowing drink*). Yes.
RANCE. Why are there so many doors. Was the house designed
by a lunatic?

PRENTICE. Yes. (*He pours another whisky.*) We have him here as a patient from time to time.

RANCE (*glancing upwards*). A skylight too? Is it functional?

PRENTICE. No. It's perfectly useless for anything – except to let light in.

> DR RANCE nods, gravely. *He wanders round the room examining everything, watched by* DR PRENTICE.

RANCE (*by the couch*). Is your couch regulation size? It looks big enough for two.

PRENTICE (*with a wary smile*). I do double consultations. Toddlers are often terrified of a doctor. So I've taken to examining their mothers at the same time.

RANCE. Has the theory received much publicity?

PRENTICE. I don't approve of scientists who publicize their theories.

RANCE. I must say I agree with you. I wish more scientists would keep their ideas to themselves.

> *A piece of paper flutters from under the curtain.*

RANCE (*picking up the paper*). Is this something to do with you, Prentice?

PRENTICE. It's a prescription, sir.

RANCE (*reading*). 'Keep your head down and don't make a sound'? (*Pause.*) Do you find your patients react favourably to such treatment?

PRENTICE. I can claim to have had some success with it.

RANCE (*drily*). Your ideas, I think, are in advance of the times.

> *He opens the curtains and closes them again, rapidly. He turns to* DR PRENTICE, *startled.*

RANCE. There's a naked woman behind there.

PRENTICE. She's a patient, sir. I'd just managed to calm her down when you arrived.

RANCE. You were attacked by a naked woman?

PRENTICE. Yes.

RANCE. Well, Prentice, I don't know whether to applaud your daring or envy you your luck. Let's take a glance at her.

DR PRENTICE *goes to the curtains.*

PRENTICE. Miss Barclay, a gentleman wishes to speak to you.

GERALDINE (*looking over the curtain*). I can't meet anyone without my clothes on, doctor.

PRENTICE (*coolly, to* DR RANCE). Notice the obstinacy with which she clings to her suburban upbringing.

RANCE. Have you tried shock treatment?

PRENTICE. No.

RANCE. How long has she been a patient?

PRENTICE. The committal order hasn't yet been signed.

RANCE. Bring it here. I'll sign it.

DR PRENTICE *goes to the desk.* DR RANCE *turns to* GERAL-DINE, *and addresses her in a brusque manner.*

RANCE. Why did you take your clothes off? Did it never occur to you that your psychiatrist might be embarrassed by your behaviour?

GERALDINE. I'm not a patient. I'm from the Friendly Faces Employment Bureau.

RANCE (*over his shoulder to* DR PRENTICE). When did those delusions first manifest themselves?

PRENTICE (*returning with a document*). I've been aware of them for some time, sir.

RANCE (*to* GERALDINE). Do you imagine that any business-man would tolerate a naked typist in his office?

GERALDINE *smiles and, in a reasonable manner, attempts to explain.*

GERALDINE. Dr Prentice asked me to undress in order that he might discover my fitness for the tasks ahead. There was no suggestion of my working permanently without clothing.

RANCE (*to* DR PRENTICE). I shall take charge of this case. It appears to have the bizarre quality that makes for a fascinating thesis. (*He signs the document.*) Make the necessary entry in your register and alert the dispensary of my requirements.

DR PRENTICE *goes into the dispensary with the document.* DR RANCE *turns to* GERALDINE.

RANCE. Is there a history of mental illness in your family?

GERALDINE (*primly*). I find your questions irrelevant. I refuse to answer them.

RANCE. I've just certified you insane. You know that, don't you?

GERALDINE *gives a gasp of surprise, and draws back from* DR RANCE.

GERALDINE. What right have you to take such high-handed action?

RANCE. Every right. You've had a nervous breakdown.

GERALDINE. I'm quite sane!

RANCE. Pull yourself together. Why have you been certified if you're sane? Even for a madwoman you're unusually dense.

DR PRENTICE *enters from the dispensary wheeling a hospital trolley. On it is a rubber mattress, a pillow and a blanket. Over his arm* DR PRENTICE *carries a white hospital nightgown.* DR RANCE *takes this from him. He throws it over the curtain to* GERALDINE.

RANCE. Put that on!

GERALDINE (*to* DR RANCE). Oh, thank you. It's a great relief to be clothed again.

DR RANCE *draws* DR PRENTICE *aside.* GERALDINE *puts on the nightgown.*

RANCE. What is the background of this case? Has the patient any family?

PRENTICE. No, sir. Her step-mother died recently after

a remarkably intimate involvement with Sir Winston Churchill.

RANCE. What of the father?

PRENTICE. He appears to have been an unpleasant fellow. He made her mother pregnant at her place of employment.

RANCE. Was there any reason for such conduct?

PRENTICE. The patient is reticent on the subject.

RANCE. I find that strange. And very revealing. (*He opens the curtains on the couch. To* GERALDINE.) Lie on this trolley. (*To* DR PRENTICE.) Go and prepare a sedative.

DR PRENTICE *goes into the dispensary.* DR RANCE *helps* GERALDINE *from the couch.*

GERALDINE. Please ring for a taxi, sir. I wish to return home. I haven't the qualities required for this job.

RANCE (*lifting her on to the trolley and covering her with the blanket*). You're slowing down your recovery rate, Miss Barclay.

DR PRENTICE *enters from the dispensary with a kidney-shaped bowl, swabs and a hypodermic syringe.* DR RANCE *bares* GERALDINE's *arm, and wipes it with a swab.*

GERALDINE (*appealing to* DR PRENTICE). Tell him the truth, doctor! I'm a fully qualified shorthand-typist!

DR RANCE *gives her an injection. She gasps, and bursts into tears.*

GERALDINE. This is intolerable! You're a disgrace to your profession! I shall ring the B.M.A. after lunch.

RANCE. Accept your condition without tears and without abusing those placed in authority. (*He puts the hypodermic aside, and goes to wash his hands.*)

MRS PRENTICE *enters from the hall.*

MRS PRENTICE (*anxious*). Miss Barclay is nowhere to be found.

RANCE. She's under strong sedation and on no account to be disturbed.

DR PRENTICE, *nervous, gives a fleeting smile in* DR RANCE's *direction.*

PRENTICE. My wife is talking of my secretary, sir. She's been missing for some time.

GERALDINE. I'm Geraldine Barclay. Looking for part-time secretarial work. I've been certified insane.

RANCE (*to* MRS PRENTICE). Ignore these random reflections. They're an essential factor in the patient's condition. (*To* DR PRENTICE.) Does she have the same name as your secretary?

PRENTICE. She's taken my secretary's name as her 'nom-de-folie'. Although morally reprehensible, there's little we can do legally, I'm afraid.

RANCE (*drying his hands*). It seems a trifle capricious, but the insane are famous for their wild ways.

MRS PRENTICE. I shall contact the employment agency. Miss Barclay can't have vanished into thin air.

She goes into the hall. DR PRENTICE *pours himself a drink.*

PRENTICE. My wife is unfamiliar with the habits of young women, sir. I've known many who could vanish into thin air. And some who took a delight in doing so.

DR RANCE *puts on a white coat.*

RANCE. In my experience young women vanish only at midnight and after a heavy meal. (*He buttons the coat.*) Were your relations with your secretary normal?

PRENTICE. Yes.

RANCE. Well, Prentice, your private life is your own affair. I find it shocking none the less. Did the patient know of your liaison with Miss Barclay?

PRENTICE. She may have done.

RANCE. I see. A definite pattern is beginning to emerge.

He returns to the trolley and stands looking down at GERAL-DINE.

Under the influence of the drug I've administered, Miss Barclay, you are relaxed and unafraid. I'm going to ask you some questions which I want answered in a clear non-technical style. (*To* DR PRENTICE.) She'll take that as an invitation to use bad language. (*To* GERALDINE.) Who was the first man in your life?

GERALDINE. My father.

RANCE. Did he assault you?

GERALDINE. No!

RANCE (*to* DR PRENTICE). She may mean 'Yes' when she says 'No'. It's elementary feminine psychology. (*To* GERALDINE.) Was your step-mother aware of your love for your father?

GERALDINE. I lived in a normal family. I had no love for my father.

RANCE (*to* DR PRENTICE). I'd take a bet that she was the victim of an incestuous attack. She clearly associates violence and the sexual act. Her attempt, when naked, to provoke you to erotic response may have deeper significance. (*To* GERALDINE.) Did your father have any religious beliefs?

GERALDINE. I'm sure he did.

RANCE (*to* DR PRENTICE). Yet she claims to have lived in a normal family. The depth of her condition can be measured from such a statement. (*To* GERALDINE.) Did your father's church sanction rape? (*To* DR PRENTICE.) Some sects will turn a blind eye to anything as long as it's kept within the family circle. (*To* GERALDINE.) Was there a Church service before you were assaulted?

GERALDINE. I can't answer these questions, sir. They seem pointless and disgusting.

RANCE. I'm interested in rape, Miss Barclay, not the aesthetics of cross-examination. Answer me, please! Were you molested by your father?

GERALDINE (*with a scream of horror*). No, no, no!

DR RANCE *straightens up and faces* DR PRENTICE.

RANCE. The vehemence of her denials is proof positive of guilt.

It's a text-book case! A man beyond innocence, a girl aching for experience. The beauty, confusion and urgency of their passion driving them on. They embark on a reckless love-affair. He finds it difficult to reconcile his guilty secret with his spiritual convictions. It preys on his mind. Sexual activity ceases. She, who basked in his love, feels anxiety at its loss. She seeks advice from her priest. The Church, true to Her ancient traditions, counsels chastity. The result – madness.

He puts the swabs and the hypodermic into the kidney-shaped bowl.

PRENTICE. It's a fascinating theory, sir, and cleverly put together. Does it tie in with known facts?

DR RANCE *picks up the bowl.*

RANCE. That need not cause us undue anxiety. Civilizations have been founded and maintained on theories which refused to obey facts. As far as I'm concerned this child was un-naturally assaulted by her own father. I shall base my future actions upon that assumption.

He goes into the dispensary taking the bowl, swabs and hypo-dermic with him.

GERALDINE (*pause*). Am I mad, doctor?
PRENTICE. No.
GERALDINE. Are you mad?
PRENTICE. No.
GERALDINE. Is it the candid camera?
PRENTICE. There's a perfectly rational explanation for what is taking place. Keep calm. All will be well.

DR RANCE *re-enters.*

RANCE. It's also obvious to the meanest amateur, Prentice, that you resemble the patient's father. That is why she undressed herself. When I arrived on the scene she was about to re-enact the initial experience with her parent. The vexed question of motive is now clear. She was aware of the understanding that exists between you and your secretary. You represent her father. Her identification with Miss Barclay completes the picture.

He releases the wheel-lock on the trolley.

PRENTICE. Perhaps there's a simpler explanation for the apparent complexities of the case, sir.

RANCE. Simple explanations are for simple minds. I've no use for either. (*He pushes the trolley towards the ward door.*) Open the door. I shall supervise the cutting of the patient's hair.

DR PRENTICE *opens the ward door.* DR RANCE *wheels* GERALDINE *into the ward.* DR PRENTICE *goes to the desk, pours himself a drink and swallows it quickly. His glance falls on to the wastepaper basket. He shakes out* GERALDINE'*s underclothes, sees her shoes and stockings and picks them up.* MRS PRENTICE *enters from the hall.* DR PRENTICE *swings round, turns his back on her and walks away, bent double in an effort to conceal the clothing.*

MRS PRENTICE (*alarmed by this strange conduct*). What's the matter? (*She approaches.*) Are you in pain?

PRENTICE (*his back to her, strangled*). Yes. Get me a glass of water.

MRS PRENTICE *hurries into the dispensary.* DR PRENTICE *stares about him in desperation. He sees a tall vase of roses. He removes the roses and stuffs the underclothing and one shoe into the vase. The second shoe won't go in. He pauses, perplexed. He is about to replace the roses when* MRS PRENTICE *enters carrying a glass of water.* DR PRENTICE *conceals the shoe under his coat.* MRS PRENTICE *stares. He is holding the roses. He gives a feeble smile and presents them to her with a flourish.* MRS PRENTICE *is surprised and angry.*

MRS PRENTICE. Put them back at once!

The shoe slips and DR PRENTICE, *in an effort to retain it, doubles up.*

Should I call a doctor?

PRENTICE. No. I'll be all right.

MRS PRENTICE (*offering him the glass*). Here. Drink this.

DR PRENTICE backs away, still holding the roses and the shoe.

PRENTICE. I wonder if you'd get another glass? That one is quite the wrong shape.

MRS PRENTICE (*puzzled*). The wrong shape?

PRENTICE. Yes.

MRS PRENTICE stares hard at him, then goes into the dispensary. DR PRENTICE tries to replace the roses in the vase. They won't go in. He picks up a pair of scissors from his desk and cuts the stalks down to within an inch or so of the heads. He puts the roses into the vase and wraps the stalks in his handkerchief and puts it into his pocket. He looks for somewhere to conceal the second shoe. He gets on his knees and shoves the shoe between the space on top of the books on the lower shelf of the bookcase. MRS PRENTICE enters carrying another glass. She stops and stares.

MRS PRENTICE. What are you doing now?

PRENTICE (*lifting his hands*). Praying.

MRS PRENTICE. This puerile behaviour ill accords with your high academic standards. (*She puts the glass of water down, and tosses her head.*) The youth I wish you to engage as your secretary has arrived.

PRENTICE (*drinking water*). Perhaps he'd call back later. I'm still feeling dicky.

MRS PRENTICE. I'll see what he says. He's an impatient young man.

PRENTICE. Is that why he took to rape?

MRS PRENTICE. Yes. He can't wait for anything.

She hurries away into the hall. DR PRENTICE wipes his brow.

PRENTICE. Two decades spent fighting her and a receding hairline! I've had just about enough of both.

DR RANCE *enters from the ward.*

RANCE. You'll have no trouble recognizing the patient, Prentice. I've clipped her hair to within an inch of the scalp.

PRENTICE (*shocked*). Was it quite wise to do that, sir? Is it in accord with the present enlightened approach to the mentally sick?

RANCE. Perfectly in accord. I've published a monograph on the subject. I wrote it at University. On the advice of my tutor. A remarkable man. Having failed to achieve madness himself he took to teaching it to others.

PRENTICE. And you were his prize pupil?

RANCE. There were some more able than I.

PRENTICE. Where are they now?

RANCE. In mental institutions.

PRENTICE. Running them?

RANCE. For the most part.

MRS PRENTICE *enters from the hall.*

MRS PRENTICE (*to* DR PRENTICE). He insists upon punctuality. He'll give you five minutes.

PRENTICE (*to* DR RANCE). A prospective employee, sir. It's useless to claim that Socialism has had no effect.

RANCE (*to* MRS PRENTICE). Is there no news of Miss Barclay?

MRS PRENTICE. None. I've checked with the Employment Bureau. Their clients have strict instructions to ring them immediately after an interview. Miss Barclay has failed to do so.

RANCE. A search party must be organized. (*To* DR PRENTICE.) What have you in the way of dogs?

PRENTICE. A spaniel and a miniature poodle.

RANCE. Let them be unleashed! Geraldine Barclay must be found or the authorities informed.

MRS PRENTICE. I'll contact the warden. He has charge of the gate and will know whether she left the building. (*She turns to go.*)

PRENTICE. No – don't do that. Miss Barclay is quite safe. She's downstairs. I've just remembered.

RANCE (*pause, surprised*). Why did you keep the fact from us?

PRENTICE. It'd slipped my memory.

RANCE. Have you suffered from lapses of memory before?

PRENTICE. I can't remember.

RANCE. Your memory plays you false even on the subject of its own inadequacy?

PRENTICE. I may have had a blackout. I don't recall having one on any other occasion.

RANCE. You might have forgotten. You admit your memory isn't reliable.

PRENTICE. I can only state what I know, sir. I can't be expected to remember things I've forgotten.

MRS PRENTICE. What's Miss Barclay doing downstairs?

PRENTICE. She's making white golliwogs for sale in colour-prejudice trouble-spots.

DR RANCE *and* MRS PRENTICE *exchange startled looks.*

RANCE. You claim, Prentice, that you forgot your secretary was manufacturing these monstrosities?

PRENTICE. Yes.

RANCE. I can hardly credit it. Once seen a white golliwog is not easily forgotten. What was the object in creating these nightmare creatures?

PRENTICE. I hoped it might promote racial harmony.

RANCE. These hellish white homuncules must be put out of their misery. I order you to destroy them before their baleful influence can make itself felt.

PRENTICE (*wearily*). I'll get Miss Barclay to carry out your orders, sir.

He goes out by the ward door. DR RANCE *turns to* MRS PRENTICE *and mops his brow.*

RANCE. The man's a second Frankenstein.

MRS PRENTICE *goes to the desk and pours herself a whisky.*

MRS PRENTICE (*with a half-smile*). My husband is a strange person, doctor. Is he a genius or merely a highly-strung fool?

RANCE. I'd like to know him better before I ventured an opinion. Have there been other schemes besides this golliwog scandal?

MRS PRENTICE (*drinking whisky*). His letters to the newspapers are legion.

She takes her drink to the bookcase. She lifts, from the bottom shelf, a leather-bound cuttings book.

(*Opening the book and showing it to* DR RANCE.) From his first letter, at the age of twelve, complaining of inaccurate information given to him by a German child whilst they were playing 'mothers and fathers' – he speculates on the nature and extent of Nazi propaganda.

DR RANCE *stares hard at the book.* MRS PRENTICE *turns the pages.*

To his latest letter, published a month ago, in which he calls Gentlemen's Lavatories 'the last stronghold of male privilege . . .'

DR RANCE, *after reading, hands the book back.*

RANCE. Your husband's behaviour gives me cause for grave disquiet. Are you yourself convinced that his methods can result in a lessening of tension between the sane and the insane?

MRS PRENTICE. The purpose of my husband's clinic isn't to cure, but to liberate and exploit madness.

RANCE. In this he appears to succeed only too well. (*He faces her, candidly.*) Never have I seen matters conducted as they are in this house.

He takes a piece of paper from his pocket and hands it to her.

Read that.

MRS PRENTICE (*reading*). 'Keep your head down and don't make a sound'? (*Handing it back.*) What does it mean?

RANCE. Your husband is using dangerously unorthodox methods in his treatment of the insane. (*He goes to his briefcase and puts the note away.*)

MRS PRENTICE *frowns and puts the glass down.*

MRS PRENTICE. I hesitate to mention this, doctor – as a wife my loyalties are involved – but I must confess that only this morning my husband announced his intention of using Thomas Hardy to cure a disorder of the bladder.

RANCE (*grimly*). As a psychiatrist your husband seems not only ineffective, but also undesirable.

MRS PRENTICE *takes the cuttings book back to the bookcase and attempts to put the book away. She is unable to do so. She investigates. She discovers* GERALDINE's *shoe and looks at it in amazement.*

MRS PRENTICE. What a thing to find in a bookcase!

RANCE (*pause*). Is it yours?

MRS PRENTICE. No.

RANCE. Let me see it.

She hands him the shoe. He turns it over in his hand.

RANCE (*looking up, after a pause*). I must ask you to be honest with me, Mrs Prentice. Has Dr Prentice at any time given you cause to doubt his own sanity?

MRS PRENTICE *gives a quick gasp of fear, rising to her feet.*

MRS PRENTICE. He's a respected member of his profession. His work in all fields has been praised by numerous colleagues.

RANCE. Radical thought comes easily to the lunatic.

MRS PRENTICE (*pause*). You're quite right. (*She dabs at her nose with a handkerchief.*) I've known for some time that all was not well. I've tried to convince myself that my fears were groundless. All the while I knew I was cheating myself.

DR RANCE *leads her to a chair. She sits, overcome by shock.*

RANCE (*quietly*). What first aroused your suspicions?

MRS PRENTICE. Oh, I think his boorish attitude towards my mother. He used to ring her up and suggest painful ways of committing suicide. Worn out at last by his pestering she took his advice.

RANCE. And more recently, say from this morning, has there been an increase in his condition?

MRS PRENTICE. Oh, yes. Quite definitely, doctor. He had no sympathy for me when I complained of being assaulted by a page-boy at the Station Hotel.

RANCE. What was the object of the assault?

MRS PRENTICE. The youth wanted to rape me.

RANCE. He didn't succeed?

MRS PRENTICE. No.

RANCE (*shaking his head*). The service in these hotels is dreadful.

MRS PRENTICE. Shortly after my return my husband started having the most extraordinary ideas which I'd've been willing to indulge if they hadn't overstepped the bounds of good taste.

RANCE. Give me an example.

MRS PRENTICE. He has developed a craving for women's clothes.

RANCE (*picking up* GERALDINE'*s shoe*). This confirms your story.

MRS PRENTICE. I refused to loan him any of mine and went in search of Miss Barclay. Some time later, in my presence, my husband had a kind of fit. He asked me to get him a drink. When I returned he presented me with a bouquet of flowers.

RANCE. He wished to congratulate you on your safe return.

MRS PRENTICE. I'd only been to the dispensary. And he'd taken the flowers from the vase. (*She points to the vase.*) I was angry and not a little frightened. At this point a spasm of agony crossed his otherwise tranquil features. I offered him the glass of water. He reacted in a violent manner. He said the glass was the wrong shape.

RANCE. What a revealing phrase!

MRS PRENTICE. I returned to the dispensary. When I got back he was on his knees praying.

RANCE. How shocking! His abnormal condition has driven him to seek refuge in religion. Always the last ditch stand of a man on the brink of disaster. (*He pats* MRS PRENTICE *on the shoulder.*) I can't doubt that what you've told me has great significance. We must also take into account his admitted lapse of memory, and the attempts to create alien forms of life. (*He puts the shoe into his case.*) Say nothing of our suspicions. Fancies grow like weeds in the unhealthy soil of a sick brain.

MRS PRENTICE (*dabbing her eyes with a handkerchief*). Oh, doctor, you've no idea what a relief it's been to talk to someone like yourself.

RANCE. Why haven't you done so before?

MRS PRENTICE. A woman doesn't like facing the fact that the man she loves is insane. It makes her look such a fool.

She puts the handkerchief away, pours herself a drink and drops ice into the glass. DR PRENTICE *enters from the ward.*

RANCE (*turning to him*). Have you carried out my instructions?

PRENTICE. Yes.

RANCE. You guilty scientists will destroy the world with your shameful secrets. (*He takes* GERALDINE's *shoe from his briefcase.*) Does this belong to your secretary?

PRENTICE. No. (*Pause.*) It's mine.

DR RANCE *and* MRS PRENTICE *exchange looks.* DR RANCE *raises an eyebrow.*

RANCE (*heavily, with irony*). Are you in the habit of wearing women's footwear?

PRENTICE (*quickly, desperate*). My private life is my own. Society must not be too harsh in its judgements.

DR RANCE *puts the shoe aside.*

RANCE. Where is this secretary of yours? I've a few questions I'd like to put to her.

PRENTICE. I can't allow you to disturb her. She has work to do.

DR RANCE *gives a humourless smile.*

RANCE. I don't think you quite appreciate the position, Prentice. The powers vested in me by the Commissioners give the right to interview any member of your staff should occasion demand. Where is Geraldine Barclay?

PRENTICE. She's in the garden.

RANCE. Ask her to step this way.

PRENTICE. She's making a funeral pyre for the golliwogs. It would be wrong to disturb her.

RANCE. Very well. (*Tight-lipped.*) I shall seek her out myself. You may be sure, Prentice, your conduct won't go unreported!

He goes into the garden. DR PRENTICE *turns on his wife in cold fury.*

PRENTICE. What've you told him?

MRS PRENTICE. Nothing but the truth.

PRENTICE (*pouring a drink*). You've been spreading it around that I'm a transvestite, haven't you?

MRS PRENTICE. There was a woman's shoe hidden in the bookcase. What was it doing there?

PRENTICE. Why were you rooting among my books?

MRS PRENTICE. I was looking for the cuttings album. I showed it to Dr Rance.

PRENTICE. You'd no right to do that.

MRS PRENTICE. Are you ashamed of the fact that you write to strange men?

PRENTICE. There's nothing furtive in my relationship with the editor of *The Guardian*.

MRS PRENTICE *pours herself another drink.*

MRS PRENTICE. Dr Rance and I are trying to help you. We're not satisfied with your condition.

PRENTICE. Neither am I. It's impossible and you're to blame. I should've driven you out with ignominy years ago.

MRS PRENTICE *puts the empty whisky bottle aside and turns on* DR PRENTICE *resentfully.*

MRS PRENTICE. Whose fault is it if our marriage is on the rocks? You're selfish and inconsiderate. Don't push me too far. (*With a toss of her head.*) I might sleep with someone else.

PRENTICE. Who?

MRS PRENTICE. An Indian student.

PRENTICE. You don't know any.

MRS PRENTICE. New Delhi is full of them.

PRENTICE (*staring, aghast*). You can't take lovers in Asia! The air fare would be crippling.

MRS PRENTICE *drops ice into her glass and ignores* DR PRENTICE, *her nose in the air.* DR PRENTICE *stands beside her and shouts into her ear.*

Your irresponsible behaviour causes me untold anxiety. A man exposed himself to you last summer.

MRS PRENTICE (*without looking at him*). I didn't see anything.

PRENTICE. And your disappointment marred our holiday.

MRS PRENTICE. You've no psychological understanding of the difficulties I face. (*She drinks whisky.*)

PRENTICE (*pulling her round, white with rage*). Unless you're very careful you'll find yourself in a suitcase awaiting collection!

MRS PRENTICE *laughs, sharply.*

MRS PRENTICE. These veiled threats confirm the doubts I already have of your sanity.

She drinks the whisky and walks away from DR PRENTICE *who scowls at her.* NICK *enters from the hall. He carries a slim cardboard box with the words* 'STATION HOTEL' *printed on it.*

NICK (*to* MRS PRENTICE). If you'll hand over the money, madam, I'll let you have the photos. However, some guarantee of employment must be given before I part with the negatives.

DR PRENTICE, *puzzled, turns to* MRS PRENTICE.

PRENTICE. What's he talking about?

MRS PRENTICE. He has in his possession a series of pornographic studies of me. He took them last night without my knowledge.

DR PRENTICE *turns away, weary, almost in tears.*

PRENTICE. Oh, the damnable frivolity of the woman! I shall have to turn paederast to get her out of this mess. (*He passes a hand across his brow.*)

NICK *presents* MRS PRENTICE *with the box.*

NICK. I have to deliver this. It's from our two-hour cleaning service.

MRS PRENTICE *opens the box.*

MRS PRENTICE (*with delight*). My dress and wig!

DR PRENTICE *narrows his eyes and gives a brief exclamation.*

PRENTICE. A dress? I'll take possession of that. (*He takes the box from her.*)

MRS PRENTICE. I shall inform Dr Rance of your theft of one of my dresses. (*She spits the words into his astonished face.*)

PRENTICE. Don't raise your voice. Take a biscuit from the barrel and retire to your room.

MRS PRENTICE *tosses her head, picks a full bottle of whisky from the desk and flounces into the hall.*

NICK. I'm sorry if my behaviour last night caused your wife anxiety, but I've a burning desire to sleep with every woman I meet.

PRENTICE. That's a filthy habit and, in my opinion, very injurious to the health.

NICK. It is, sir. My health's never been the same since I went off stamp-collecting.

DR PRENTICE *puts the box on to the desk and pours himself a drink.*

PRENTICE. We have an overall moral policy in this clinic from which even I am not exempt. Whilst you're with us I shall expect you to show an interest in no one's sexual organs but your own.

NICK. I would miss a lot of fun that way.

PRENTICE. That is the object of the exercise.

DR RANCE *enters from the garden.*

RANCE. I can find no trace of your secretary. I might add, Prentice, that my patience is all but exhausted.

PRENTICE. She might be in the dispensary.

RANCE. Unless I discover her whereabouts within the next few minutes you'll find yourself in serious trouble.

He goes into the dispensary. MRS PRENTICE *enters from the hall.*

MRS PRENTICE. A policeman is at the door. He wishes to speak to some member of the household.

PRENTICE. Ask him to step this way.

MRS PRENTICE *goes into the hall.* NICK *stands and appeals to* DR PRENTICE, *emotional.*

NICK. Oh, sir! They've come to arrest me!

PRENTICE. This paranoia is uncalled-for. The officer has

probably called to ask me for the hand of my cook in marriage.

NICK. You're wrong, sir! They'll give me five years if I'm caught.

PRENTICE. Why are you in danger of arrest. You may be quite frank with me.

NICK. Well, sir, as your wife has already told you, I attempted last night to misbehave myself with her. I didn't succeed.

PRENTICE. I'm sure you didn't. Despite all appearances to the contrary, Mrs Prentice is harder to get into than the reading room at the British Museum.

NICK. Undeterred I took the lift to the third floor of the hotel where a party of schoolgirls were staying. Oh, sir, what lonely and aimless lives they lead!

PRENTICE (*with a frown*). Was there no mistress in attendance?

NICK. She occupied a room across the corridor.

PRENTICE. Did you disturb her?

NICK. No. And she'll never forgive me for it. It was she who reported the incident to the police. Oh, sir! Don't turn me over to the law.

DR RANCE *enters from the dispensary.*

RANCE. I warn you, Prentice, unless you're prepared to co-operate in finding Miss Barclay I shall call upon you to account for her disappearance. If you're unable to do so the police must be informed.

He goes into the ward.

NICK. Have you given a thought to my predicament?

PRENTICE. No. I'm obsessed by my own. (*He wipes his brow.*) We shall be sharing the same cell at this rate.

His eye lights on the cardboard box. He turns to NICK, *an idea dawning.*

(*Abruptly.*) Take your clothes off.

NICK (*pause*). Are you going to mess me about, sir?

PRENTICE. Certainly not! Is that what usually happens when men ask you to take your clothes off?

NICK. Yes. They give me five shillings.

PRENTICE. Five shillings! Good gracious the rate hasn't changed in thirty years. What can the unions be thinking of? (*He puts a hand on* NICK's *shoulder*.) Come along, strip!

NICK *tugs at a zip. The jacket opens from shoulder to hip. He takes it off, kicks away his shoes and drops his trousers.* DR PRENTICE *stares in admiration.*

PRENTICE. Remarkable. My last secretary couldn't better you. And she was a descendant of Houdini.

NICK *hands the clothes to* DR PRENTICE. *He is naked except for a pair of shorts. He is about to take them off when* DR PRENTICE *holds up his hand.*

Don't remove your drawers. My medical training has familiarized me with what is underneath.

MRS PRENTICE *enters from the hall. She stops in horror.*

MRS PRENTICE. What devilry are you up to now?

PRENTICE. I'm carrying out a medical examination.

MRS PRENTICE. But you're not a physician. Why do you need the child undressed?

PRENTICE (*smiling, with enormous patience*). My investigations upon his clothed body would be strictly 'unscientific' and, inevitably, superficial. In order to assure myself that he's going to be of use to me I must examine him fully. And skin-wise.

MRS PRENTICE. You ogre! Never, in my whole life, have I heard anything so lame and stupid. This folly will get you struck off the Register. (*Picking up* NICK's *uniform*.) Come with me, dear. You mustn't be left with this man.

She takes the uniform into the hall.

NICK. What do we do now, sir? If the law comes I can't even run for it.

DR PRENTICE *picks up the cardboard box and takes out a leopard-spotted dress and a wig.*

PRENTICE. I have an idea. I want you to impersonate my secretary. Her name is Geraldine Barclay. It will solve all our problems if you agree to my request.

He gives NICK *the dress and wig.*

It's of particular importance to convince Dr Rance that you're a woman. You should encounter no real difficulties there. He's an elderly man. I don't suppose he's checked with the original lately.

He takes NICK *to the dispensary door.*

After your meeting plead illness and leave the house. I'll be waiting with your own clothes. The operation completed you'll be given a sum of money and a ticket for any destination you choose. (*Pushing him into the dispensary.*) If you run into trouble I shall deny all knowledge of you. Dress in there.

He shuts the dispensary door, goes to the hall and calls in friendly tones:

Would you like to step this way, officer? I'm sorry to have kept you waiting.

He goes to the desk and opens a fresh bottle of whisky. NICK *opens the dispensary door and looks through.*

NICK. Shoes, sir!

DR PRENTICE *swings round in alarm.*

PRENTICE. Shoes! (*He puts the bottle down.*) One moment!

He takes GERALDINE's *shoe from* DR RANCE's *brief-case and throws it to* NICK. *He goes to the vase and lifts the roses quickly. He puts a hand into the vase, searching for the other shoe.* SERGEANT MATCH *enters.* NICK *darts into the dispensary.* DR PRENTICE *puts the roses behind his back.*

(*In cold tones.*) Would you mind not entering my consulting room without permission?

MATCH (*a little put out*). You asked me to come in, sir.

PRENTICE. I don't believe I did. Wait outside.

SERGEANT MATCH *leaves the room.* DR PRENTICE *shakes* GERALDINE's *shoe from the vase. He hurries to the dispensary, throws the shoe inside and darts back to the vase. He is about to replace the flowers when* MRS PRENTICE *enters from the hall. She sees* DR PRENTICE *is holding the flowers and steps back in amazement.* DR PRENTICE *offers her the bunch of roses. Her face turns ashen. She is angry and a little frightened.*

MRS PRENTICE. Why do you keep giving me flowers?

PRENTICE. It's because I'm very fond of you, my dear.

MRS PRENTICE. Your actions grow wilder with every passing moment. Why were you rude to the policeman?

PRENTICE. He barged in without so much as a by-your-leave.

MRS PRENTICE. But you asked him to come in. Had you forgotten?

PRENTICE. Yes. (*Pause.*) My memory isn't what it was. Tell him I'll see him now.

MRS PRENTICE *goes into the hall.* DR PRENTICE *replaces the flowers, goes to his desk and pours a large whisky.* GERALDINE *enters from the ward. Her hair has been cut short. She is wearing the hospital nightdress.* DR PRENTICE *is considerably alarmed by her presence in the room.*

Miss Barclay! What are you doing here?

GERALDINE. Nothing would induce me to remain on your staff a moment longer, doctor. I wish to give notice.

SERGEANT MATCH *enters from the hall. His view of* GERALDINE *is obscured by the couch.*

MATCH. Sorry for the misunderstanding, sir.

PRENTICE (*turning, abrupt*). Please remain outside. I think I made myself plain.

MATCH (*pause*). You don't wish to see me?

PRENTICE. No.

> SERGEANT MATCH, *somewhat perplexed by the situation, goes into the hall.* DR PRENTICE *takes* GERALDINE *by the arm.*

Your disclosures could ruin me. Give me a chance to get us out of this mess.

GERALDINE. You must put matters right by telling the truth.

PRENTICE (*pulls curtains round couch*). Hide behind here. Nothing unpleasant will happen. You have my word as a gentleman.

GERALDINE. We must tell the truth!

PRENTICE. That's a thoroughly defeatist attitude. (*He bundles her behind the curtain.*)

GERALDINE (*looking over the curtain*). At least give me back my clothes. I feel naked without them.

> DR PRENTICE *removes the roses from the vase, takes out* GERALDINE's *underclothes and stockings and throws them to her.* MRS PRENTICE *and* SERGEANT MATCH *enter from the hall.* GERALDINE *ducks behind the curtain.* DR PRENTICE *has the roses in his hand.* MRS PRENTICE *clutches* SERGEANT MATCH's *arm.*

MRS PRENTICE. Oh, if he presents me with those flowers again I shall faint!

> *They watch in silence as* DR PRENTICE *replaces the roses with an air of confidence. Without* GERALDINE's *clothes under them the stalks are too short. The flowers vanish into the vase.* MRS PRENTICE *cries out in surprise.*

MRS PRENTICE. He's cut the stalks off! His lunacy is beyond belief.

DR PRENTICE *picks up his drink and turns, blandly, to* SERGEANT MATCH.

PRENTICE. Excuse my wife's hysteria, sergeant. A man tried to molest her last night. Her recovery is far from complete.

MATCH. I understand that Mrs Prentice introduced the young man to you, sir?

PRENTICE. Yes. We shan't prefer charges.

MATCH. I believe your wife to be ill-advised in not repeating her experiences before a judge and jury. However, as it happens, I'm not concerned with this case. I'm interested in the youth's movements between midnight and seven a.m. During that period he is alleged to have misconducted himself with a party of schoolchildren.

MRS PRENTICE (*pouring a drink*). How vile and disgraceful!

MATCH. After carrying out a medical examination our lady doctor is up in arms. She can't wait to meet this fellow face to face.

PRENTICE. Well, sergeant, he isn't on the premises. If he turns up you'll be informed.

MRS PRENTICE (*shocked*). How dare you give misleading information to the police? (*To* SERGEANT MATCH.) He was here. I have his clothes outside.

MATCH. Very wise of you to confiscate his clothing, ma'am. If more women did the same the number of cases of rape would be halved.

PRENTICE (*at the desk*). Or doubled.

MRS PRENTICE. Disregard anything my husband says. I'll fetch the clothing.

She goes into the hall carrying her drink. SERGEANT MATCH *turns to* DR PRENTICE.

MATCH. I'm also anxious, sir, to trace the whereabouts of a young woman called Barclay. Can you help in my inquiries?

PRENTICE (*a spasm of anxiety crossing his face*). Why do you wish to see Miss Barclay?

MATCH. It's a matter of national importance. Miss Barclay's step-mother, a woman of otherwise unblemished character, died recently. Shortly before her death her name had been linked in a most unpleasant way with that of Sir Winston Churchill. Mrs Barclay's association with the great man gave offence in some circles. However, the local council, composed by and large of no-nonsense men and women of the 'sixties, decided in view of his war record to overlook Sir Winston's moral lapse. Under expert guidance he was to be reintegrated into society. The task accomplished it became clear that the great man was incomplete. When the true facts got out the die-hards were in uproar. The press took up the story and it snowballed out of all proportion. At last – with the full support of the Conservative and Unionist Party – the council decided to sue the heirs of Mrs Barclay for those parts of Sir Winston which an army-type medical had proved to be missing. The council's lawyers obtained an exhumation order. This morning the coffin was opened in the presence of the Lord Mayor and Lady Mayoress of this borough. Fainting women were held back as the official in charge searched high and low for council property. His efforts were not crowned with success. Mrs Barclay had taken nothing with her to the grave except those things which she ought to have done. At noon today the matter came to the attention of the police.

PRENTICE (*pouring whisky*). You suspect my secretary of having stolen certain parts of Sir Winston Churchill?

MRS PRENTICE *enters with* NICK'S *uniform*.

MRS PRENTICE. Here is proof that the young man was in this room.

MATCH. He can't get far without clothing.

PRENTICE. His progress without clothing last night was enviable.

MATCH (*to* DR PRENTICE). You still claim, sir, that you have no knowledge of the youth's whereabouts?

PRENTICE. No.

MATCH. And what has become of Miss Barclay?

PRENTICE. I've no idea.

MRS PRENTICE. You told Dr Rance she was burning the golliwogs.

SERGEANT MATCH *looks from one to the other in amazement.*

Was that a lie?

PRENTICE. It may have been. I can't remember.

MRS PRENTICE *gives an impatient toss of her head.*

MRS PRENTICE. You must talk to Dr Rance, sergeant. He may
be able to account for my husband's unusual behaviour
pattern.

MATCH. Where would the doctor be?

MRS PRENTICE. In the garden. Please tell him that his special-
ized knowledge is urgently required.

SERGEANT MATCH *goes into the garden.* MRS PRENTICE
*turns to her husband and addresses him in unfamiliar tones of
quietness and sympathy.*

Now, darling, you've clearly lost the capacity to remember
fresh items of information, to solve unaccustomed problems
and to remain orientated. Don't let this worry you. I shall
be at your side throughout the whole course of your illness.
I'm even going to take notes on the progress of your breakdown. So nothing will be wasted. Try to remember why you
damaged the flowers in this vase. It may have a direct bearing
on the case.

*She gives a charming smile, picks up the vase and goes into the
hall.* GERALDINE *pokes her head over the curtain.*

GERALDINE. Tell the truth, sir. All your troubles spring from
a lack of candour.

PRENTICE. My troubles spring from a misguided attempt to
seduce you.

GERALDINE (*with a gasp*). You never told me you were seducing me. You said you were interested in my mind.

PRENTICE. That's like 'open sesame' – a formula for gaining entrance.

SERGEANT MATCH *appears in the french windows.* GERALDINE *ducks behind the curtain.*

MATCH. Are you sure that Dr Rance is out here, sir?

PRENTICE. Yes.

MATCH. Where would he be then?

PRENTICE. In the shrubbery. We've a naked elf on a bird-bath. We often have trouble with peeping-toms.

MATCH. I'd like you to accompany me, sir.

DR PRENTICE *shrugs and follows* SERGEANT MATCH *into the garden.* GERALDINE *steps down from the couch. She is wearing her panties and bra. She carries the nightgown. She picks up* NICK's *uniform. She drops the nightdress on to a chair and hurries to the dispensary. She retreats at once.*

GERALDINE. A strange woman!

She runs to the ward door, looks through and backs terrified.

Dr Rance! Oh, whatever shall I do?

She scurries to the hall, checks herself and scuttles back to the couch. She climbs behind the curtains. MRS PRENTICE *enters carrying the roses in a smaller vase.* NICK *enters from the dispensary. He is dressed in women's clothing and wears a blonde wig.* MRS PRENTICE *gives a gasp of surprise and puts the vase down.*

MRS PRENTICE. Are you Geraldine Barclay?

NICK. Yes. (*He speaks in low, cultured tones.*)

MRS PRENTICE. Where have you been?

NICK (*primly*). I've been attending to the thousand and one duties that occupy the average secretary during her working hours.

MRS PRENTICE. It doesn't take the whole morning to file your nails, surely?

NICK. I had to lie down. I was sick.

MRS PRENTICE. Are you pregnant?

NICK *tosses back a lock of hair.*

NICK. I can't discuss my employer's business with you.

MRS PRENTICE. What was your last job?

NICK. I was a hostess at the 'One, Two, Three' Club.

MRS PRENTICE *purses her lips in disapproval.*

MRS PRENTICE. It's obvious that you're unsuited to the work here. I shan't recommend you for employment.

DR PRENTICE *and* SERGEANT MATCH *enter from the garden.*

(*To* SERGEANT MATCH.) This is my husband's secretary, sergeant. She'll be pleased to help you in your inquiries.

MATCH (*to* NICK). Miss Barclay, I must ask you to produce or cause to be produced, the missing parts of Sir Winston Churchill.

NICK. What do they look like?

MATCH. You're claiming ignorance of the shape and structure of the objects sought?

NICK. I'm in the dark.

MATCH. You handled them only at night? We shall draw our own conclusions.

NICK. I'm not the kind of girl to be mixed-up in that kind of thing. I'm an ex-member of the Brownies.

MATCH. Are you concealing unlawful property about your person?

NICK. No.

MATCH. I'll have to call medical evidence to prove your story, miss. You must be thoroughly looked into.

PRENTICE. I'm a qualified doctor.

MATCH. Only women are permitted to examine female suspects.

PRENTICE. Doesn't that breed discontent in the force?

MATCH. Among the single men there's a certain amount of bitterness. Married men who are familiar with the country are glad to be let off extra map-reading.

MRS PRENTICE. I'll examine Miss Barclay. That will solve the problem.

MATCH. Thank you, ma'am. I accept your kind offer. Take the young lady into the dispensary and get her to submit to a medical examination.

MRS PRENTICE leads NICK into the dispensary. DR RANCE enters from the ward, his face a mask of horror.

RANCE. Prentice! The patient has escaped. Sound the alarm.

MATCH. How long has the patient been gone, sir?

RANCE. Only a few minutes.

MATCH. Any steps you feel may be necessary to recover your patient may be taken, sir.

DR RANCE crosses, pulls the siren bell and hurries into the hall.

She must've come through this room. You and I were in the garden. Mrs Prentice was in the hall. Escape would be impossible. She must still be in this room. (*He turns to DR PRENTICE in triumph.*) Only one hiding place is possible.

He pulls the curtain on the couch aside. GERALDINE is revealed. She is wearing NICK's uniform, his hat and shoes. She has on DR PRENTICE's spectacles.

MATCH (*taking in the picture at a glance*). Are you from the Station Hotel?

GERALDINE *answers in a scared voice.*

GERALDINE. Yes.

MATCH. I want a word with you, my lad. (*He takes out his note-book.*)

A siren begins to wail.

Curtain

Act Two

One minute later. The siren fades.

DR PRENTICE *opens another bottle of whisky.* GERALDINE *steps from the couch in relief.*

GERALDINE (*to* SERGEANT MATCH). You've no idea how glad I am to be arrested.

MATCH. Why?

GERALDINE. I'm in great danger.

MATCH. Who from?

GERALDINE. Dr Prentice. His conduct is scandalous. Take me to the police station. I shall prefer charges.

MATCH (*to* DR PRENTICE). Have you anything to say, sir?

PRENTICE. Yes. What this young woman claims is a tissue of lies.

SERGEANT MATCH *scratches his head.*

MATCH (*pause*). This is a boy, sir. Not a girl. If you're baffled by the difference it might be as well to approach both with caution. (*To* GERALDINE.) Let's hear what you've got to say for yourself.

GERALDINE. I came here for a job. On some pretext the doctor got me to remove my clothes. Afterwards he behaved in a strange manner.

MATCH. What did he do?

GERALDINE. He asked me to lie on that couch.

SERGEANT MATCH *glances at* DR PRENTICE *in disapproval.* DR PRENTICE *drinks whisky.* MATCH *turns to* GERALDINE.

MATCH (*quietly*). Did he, at any time, attempt to interfere with you?

PRENTICE (*putting the glass down*). You'll be disappointed, sergeant, if you imagine that boy has lost his virginity.

MATCH. I hope he'll be considerably more experienced before he loses that, sir. What reason had you for taking off his clothes?

PRENTICE. I wished to assure myself of his unquestioning obedience. I give a prize each year. I hope ultimately to tie it in with the Duke of Edinburgh's Award scheme.

MATCH. I'd prefer not to have Royalty mentioned in this context, sir. Have you been in trouble of this kind before?

PRENTICE. I'm not in trouble.

MATCH. You must realize this boy is bringing a serious charge against you?

PRENTICE. Yes. It's ridiculous. I'm a married man.

MATCH. Marriage excuses no one the freaks' roll-call.

PRENTICE. I'm a respected member of my profession. Your accusation is absurd.

MATCH. It's not for me to bring accusations in a matter I don't fully understand.

PRENTICE. The boy has an unsavoury reputation. Last night requires explaining before this morning.

GERALDINE. I had nothing to do with the disgraceful happenings at the Station Hotel.

MATCH. You deny that on the night of Thursday last you did behave in an obscene manner with a section of the Priory Road School for girls?

GERALDINE. Yes.

MATCH. Nicholas Beckett I warn you that anything you say will be taken down and may be used in evidence against you.

GERALDINE. My name isn't Nicholas Beckett.

MATCH (*pause, with a frown*). Then why d'you suppose I'd wish to arrest you?

GERALDINE. To safeguard my interests?

DR PRENTICE, *at the desk, pours whisky into a glass.*

PRENTICE. You imagine you'll be safe from acts of indecency in a police station?

GERALDINE. Of course.

PRENTICE. I wish I shared your optimism.

DR RANCE *enters from the hall.*

RANCE. Full security arrangements are in force. No one is to leave the clinic without written permission. Prentice, get your secretary to issue warrants to every member of the staff.

PRENTICE. I'll do that, sir, as soon as she's ready to resume her normal duties.

MATCH (*to* DR RANCE). Would you help us clear up a spot of bother, doctor? It's a matter of some urgency. Last night this youth assaulted a number of children. This morning he was assaulted in his turn.

RANCE (*with a shrug*). What can I say? It's an extreme case of 'be done by as you did'.

MATCH. The boy has made a serious charge against Dr Prentice. He claims he was forced to strip and lie on a couch.

RANCE (*to* DR PRENTICE). A complete list of your indiscretions would make a best-seller.

PRENTICE. It's all a dreadful mistake, sir.

RANCE. Now, Prentice, at the moment there's only one thing to advise. Absolute frankness. Have you behaved in an unseemly manner?

PRENTICE. No!

MATCH. The doctor said he wanted to put the boy in some kind of club.

RANCE. It's no good trying to do that. Boys cannot be put in the club. That's half their charm.

DR PRENTICE *passes a hand across his brow. An expression of desperate anxiety is on his face.*

PRENTICE. I'm sorry if my statement misled the sergeant. My nerves are on edge.

RANCE. You should consult a qualified psychiatrist.

PRENTICE. I am a qualified psychiatrist.

RANCE. You're a fool. That isn't quite the same thing. Though, in your case, the two may have much in common. (*To* SERGEANT MATCH.) Has the boy come to your notice before?

MATCH. Not on a case of this kind. That's why we have to be careful. As the doctor rightly says, he has an unsavoury reputation. It may be that he bears Dr Prentice a grudge.

RANCE (*to* DR PRENTICE). Perhaps this accusation springs from disappointment. It might have been wiser if you hadn't rejected the young fellow's blandishments.

PRENTICE. Unnatural vice can ruin a man.

RANCE. Ruin follows the accusation not the vice. Had you committed the act you wouldn't now be facing the charge.

PRENTICE. I couldn't commit the act. I'm a heterosexual.

RANCE. I wish you wouldn't use these Chaucerian words. It's most confusing. (*To* SERGEANT MATCH.) How do you propose to get to the bottom of this affair?

MATCH. A reputable person must examine the lad.

GERALDINE. I refuse to be examined!

MATCH. You can't refuse. You're under arrest.

GERALDINE. I'm not Nicholas Beckett. I want to be taken to prison.

MATCH. If you aren't Nicholas Beckett you can't go to prison. You're not under arrest.

GERALDINE (*pause, biting her lip*). I am Nicholas Beckett.

MATCH. Then you're under arrest. You'll submit to a medical examination.

RANCE. And I shall conduct it. The mind of the victim of this kind of assault must be considered equally with the body.

GERALDINE. I haven't been assaulted.

RANCE. Then why make such a foul accusation?

GERALDINE. I didn't accuse anyone. The sergeant made the accusation.

RANCE (*to* SERGEANT MATCH). Has Dr Prentice assaulted you too? (*To* DR PRENTICE.) Is it policemen or young boys

you're after? At your age it's high time you came to a
decision (*To* SERGEANT MATCH.) Wait outside. I shall
examine the boy and make my report. Afterwards I'll take
a look at you.

MATCH (*stunned*). At me?

RANCE. Yes. We can't be too careful.

MATCH. It seems a bit unusual, sir.

RANCE (*with a bray of laughter*). You're in a madhouse.
Unusual behaviour is the order of the day.

MATCH. Only for patients.

RANCE. We've no privileged class here. It's democratic lunacy
we practise.

SERGEANT MATCH *goes into the hall, perplexed.* DR RANCE
turns to the sink, folds back his cuffs and rinses his hands.

(*Over his shoulder.*) Take your clothes off, sonny. Lie on the
couch. (*He returns to the sink.*)

GERALDINE *clutches* DR PRENTICE *by the arm.*

GERALDINE (*in a frantic whisper*). What are we to do now? I
can't undress. He'd spot the deception at once.

PRENTICE. Keep calm! The situation, though desperate, is
by no means lost.

DR RANCE *picks up a towel and dries his hands.*

GERALDINE. I shouldn't've behaved as I did, sir. I wasn't
harmed.

RANCE. You enjoyed the experience? (*He puts the towel aside
and pulls on rubber gloves.*) Would you enjoy normal intercourse?

GERALDINE. No. I might get pregnant – (*She realizes her mistake and attempts to cover up.*) – or be the cause of pregnancy
in others.

DR RANCE, *quick to notice the error, turns to* DR PRENTICE.

RANCE. He's just given away a vital piece of information.

(*He advances on* GERALDINE.) Do you think of yourself as a girl?

GERALDINE. No.

RANCE. Why not?

GERALDINE. I'm a boy.

RANCE (*kindly*). Do you have the evidence about you?

GERALDINE (*her eyes flashing an appeal to* DR PRENTICE). I must be a boy. I like girls.

DR RANCE *stops and wrinkles his brow, puzzled.*

RANCE (*aside, to* DR PRENTICE). I can't quite follow the reasoning there.

PRENTICE. Many men imagine that a preference for women, is *ipso facto*, a proof of virility.

RANCE (*nodding, sagely*). Someone should really write a book on these folk-myths. (*To* GERALDINE.) Take your trousers down. I'll tell you which sex you belong to.

GERALDINE (*backing away*). I'd rather not know!

RANCE. You wish to remain in ignorance?

GERALDINE. Yes.

RANCE. I can't encourage you in such a self-indulgent attitude. You must face facts like the rest of us.

He forces GERALDINE *back to the couch.*

PRENTICE. You're forcing the boy to undergo a repetition of a traumatic experience, sir. He might go insane.

RANCE. This is a mental home. He couldn't choose a more appropriate place. (*To* GERALDINE.) Undress. My time is valuable.

GERALDINE, *unable to stand the ordeal any longer, cries out to* DR PRENTICE *in anguish.*

GERALDINE. I can't go on, doctor! I must tell the truth. (*To* DR RANCE.) I'm not a boy! I'm a girl!

RANCE (*to* DR PRENTICE). Excellent. A confession at last. He wishes to believe he's a girl in order to minimize the feelings of guilt after homosexual intercourse.

GERALDINE (*wild-eyed, desperate*). I pretended to be a boy. I did it to help Dr Prentice.

RANCE. How does it help a man if a girl pretends to be a boy?

GERALDINE. Wives are angry if they find their husbands have undressed and seduced a girl.

RANCE. But boys are fair game? I doubt whether your very personal view of Society would go unchallenged.

Provoked beyond endurance, GERALDINE *flings herself into* DR RANCE's *arms and cries hysterically.*

GERALDINE. Undress me then, doctor! Do whatever you like only prove that I'm a girl.

DR RANCE *pushes away and turns, frigidly to* DR PRENTICE.

RANCE. If he's going to carry on like this he'll have to be strapped down.

MRS PRENTICE *enters from the dispensary.*

MRS PRENTICE (*to* DR RANCE). Would you take a look at Miss Barclay, doctor? She refuses to undress in front of a woman.

RANCE. How about in front of a man?

MRS PRENTICE. I haven't sounded her on the subject.

RANCE. I wonder if I could tempt her. (*He chews his lip.*) I'll give it a try. She may be a nymphomaniac. (*To* DR PRENTICE.) If this lad becomes foul-mouthed keep him on the boil till I return.

He goes into the dispensary followed by MRS PRENTICE. GERALDINE *pulls herself together.*

GERALDINE. I'll go through the garden, doctor. I can get a taxi home.

PRENTICE. That isn't possible. Strict security precautions are in force until the patient is recaptured.

GERALDINE. When she is recaptured can I go?

PRENTICE. No.

GERALDINE. Why not?

PRENTICE. You *are* the patient.

> GERALDINE *gives a little cry of distress.* DR RANCE *re-enters from the dispensary removing his rubber gloves.*

RANCE. Your secretary is standing on a table fighting off any attempt to undress her. She seems incapable of conducting herself in a proper manner.

PRENTICE. She's given me no cause for complaint.

RANCE. But you expect a secretary to misbehave herself. It's a condition of employment. (*He faces* DR PRENTICE, *candidly.*) Do you realize the woman uses a razor?

PRENTICE. I see nothing remarkable in that. Mrs Prentice has occasion sometimes to remove unwanted hair.

RANCE. From her chin? (*He flings the rubber gloves aside.*) There are two sexes. The unpalatable truth must be faced. Your attempts at a merger can end only in heartbreak.

> MRS PRENTICE *enters from the dispensary leading a chastened* NICK *by the hand.*

MRS PRENTICE. Miss Barclay is calmer now, doctor. I've given her a sedative.

RANCE (*turning to* NICK, *shaking his head*). What an absorbing picture of the mind in decay.

PRENTICE. Miss Barclay is no more ill than I am.

RANCE. But your condition is worse than hers.

PRENTICE. I can't accept that.

RANCE. No madman ever accepts madness. Only the sane do that. (*To* NICK, *brusquely.*) Why won't you allow Mrs Prentice to undress you?

MRS PRENTICE. Her objections appear to be religious. She claims to be at one with God.

RANCE (*to* NICK). When were you first aware of a special relationship with the Almighty?

NICK. When I was presented with a copy of the Bible bound in calf.

RANCE. Was it an autographed copy?

NICK. I don't think God actually signed it.

RANCE. Well, of course, these things slip one's memory. Was there an inscription?

NICK. Yes.

RANCE. What did it say?

NICK. W. H. Smith & Sons.

RANCE. Oh, they count as God. You've clearly had a genuine religious experience. (*He nods to* GERALDINE.) Were you present when Dr Prentice used this youth unnaturally?

NICK. What is unnatural?

RANCE (*to* MRS PRENTICE). How disturbing the questions of the mad can be. (*To* NICK.) Suppose I made an indecent suggestion to you? If you agreed something might occur which, by and large, would be regarded as natural. If, on the other hand, I approached this child – (*He smiles at* GERAL-DINE.) – my action could result only in a gross violation of the order of things.

MRS PRENTICE (*nodding to* GERALDINE). Has my husband misbehaved with that boy?

RANCE. It's impossible to say with any degree of accuracy. He refuses to co-operate with a medical examination.

MRS PRENTICE (*to* DR PRENTICE). What happened to the other boy?

PRENTICE. Which boy?

MRS PRENTICE. The one you undressed.

RANCE. This is the boy he undressed.

MRS PRENTICE. No. He undressed the boy who made a nuisance of himself to me.

RANCE (*pause*). Isn't this the same one?

MRS PRENTICE. No.

RANCE (*staring, perplexed*). There's another boy?

MRS PRENTICE. He was being interviewed for a secretarial post. My husband made him undress.

RANCE (*coldly, to* DR PRENTICE). How long have you been a
  pervert?

PRENTICE. I'm not a pervert!

RANCE. How would you describe a man who mauls young
  boys, importunes policemen and lives on terms of intimacy
  with a woman who shaves twice a day?

PRENTICE. I'd say the man was a pervert.

RANCE. I'm glad you're beginning to face the realities of the
  situation. (*To* GERALDINE.) Who are you if you're not
  Nicholas Beckett?

GERALDINE *looks to* DR PRENTICE *and bites her lip.*

PRENTICE. His name is Gerald Barclay.

RANCE (*indicating* NICK). Is he this young woman's brother?

PRENTICE. No.

RANCE. What has happened then to Nicholas Beckett?

PRENTICE. He left an hour ago to resume his duties at the
  Station Hotel.

MRS PRENTICE. He can't have done! I took his uniform. He'd
  be naked.

PRENTICE. From what one hears of the Station Hotel the
  uniform is optional.

RANCE (*shaking his head, worried*). I hope we haven't lost
  another one. We'll be alone with our miracle drugs if many
  more go. (*To* MRS PRENTICE.) Find out whether the boy
  has returned to the hotel.

MRS PRENTICE *goes into the hall.* DR RANCE *turns to* DR
PRENTICE.

Prepare the necessary papers. I'm certifying these two.

Cries of alarm come from NICK *and* GERALDINE.

NICK. Can't you do something about him, sir? He's off his
  head.

RANCE (*sternly*). I am a representative of order, you of chaos.
  Unless that fact is faced I can never hope to cure you.

(*To* DR PRENTICE.) Make out the committal orders for me
to sign.

PRENTICE (*upset and angry*). I can't agree to such drastic
action. We've no evidence of insanity.

RANCE. I'm relieving you of your post as head of this clinic.
You'll do as I say from now on.

PRENTICE. I resent your handling of this affair, sir. I shall
make my views known to the Commissioners.

RANCE. I doubt whether the views of a madman will carry
much weight with the Commissioners.

PRENTICE. I'm not mad. It only looks that way.

RANCE. Your actions today would get the Archbishop of
Canterbury declared non-compos.

PRENTICE. I'm not the Archbishop of Canterbury.

RANCE. That will come at a later stage of your illness.

PRENTICE. Your interpretation of my behaviour is misplaced
and erroneous. If anyone borders on lunacy it's you yourself!

RANCE. Bearing in mind your abnormality that is a normal
reaction. The sane appear as strange to the mad as the mad
to the sane. Remain where you are. I shall give you a capsule.

He hurries into the dispensary.

GERALDINE (*with a sob*). Twice declared insane in one day!
And they said I'd be working for a cheerful, well-spoken
crowd. (*She blows her nose.*)

NICK. Why is he wearing my uniform?

PRENTICE. He isn't a boy. He's a girl.

GERALDINE. Why is she wearing my shoes?

PRENTICE. She isn't a girl. She's a boy. (*Pouring whisky.*) Oh,
if I live to be ninety, I'll never again attempt sexual intercourse.

NICK. If we changed clothes, sir, we could get things back to
normal.

PRENTICE. We'd then have to account for the disappearance
of my secretary and the page-boy.

GERALDINE. But they don't exist!

PRENTICE. When people who don't exist disappear the account of their departure must be convincing.

NICK (*pause*). Is the sergeant corruptible?

PRENTICE. No.

NICK. I must have his uniform.

PRENTICE. Why?

NICK. To arrest myself.

DR PRENTICE *passes a hand across his forehead, dazed and weary.*

PRENTICE. I've been too long among the mad to know what sanity is.

NICK. Once I'm arrested we can write me off.

GERALDINE. You're multiplying our problems not dividing them.

NICK (*to* DR PRENTICE). Some glib pretext will get her out of the way. Then we can change clothes.

PRENTICE (*pause, uneasy*). The dangers of the cure may outweigh the disease.

DR RANCE *enters from the dispensary. He hands a bright red pill-box to* DR PRENTICE.

RANCE. Take two of these.

PRENTICE (*looking at the pill-box*). What are they?

RANCE. Dangerous drugs intended to relieve your pathologically elevated mood. Be careful not to exceed the stated dose. (*To* NICK.) Get a grip on yourself, young woman, and release those objects for which the police of five counties are searching. (*He takes* GERALDINE *by the arm.*) I'm putting this youth into a padded cell. Rampant hermaphroditism must be discouraged.

GERALDINE. Oh, I'm glad my parents are dead. This would've killed them.

DR RANCE *takes her into the ward.*

PRENTICE (*to* NICK). I'll get the sergeant to undress. I'm sus-
pected of the offence, I might as well commit it.

NICK. Can't you give him a shot of something, sir ? To damp
him down ?

PRENTICE. A mild tranquillizer wouldn't harm him, I suppose. You'll find a box of anti-depressants in my desk.

NICK *goes to the desk and takes a square, white pill-box from
the drawer.* DR PRENTICE *opens the hall door.*

(*Calling, friendly.*) Would you step this way, sergeant ?

NICK *hands* DR PRENTICE *the white pill-box and enters the
dispensary.* SERGEANT MATCH *enters from the hall.*

MATCH. You wish to speak to me, doctor ?

PRENTICE. Yes. I'd like you to undress and lie on that couch.

MATCH (*pause*). I haven't been interfered with.

PRENTICE. Never mind about that. Strip down to your underwear.

MATCH (*sitting on couch, unlacing boots*). If you make any
attempt to arouse me, doctor, I shall call for help.

PRENTICE. It's easy to see why you've never been interfered
with. You place too many obstacles in the way.

SERGEANT MATCH *takes off his boots.* NICK *appears in the
doorway of the dispensary.* DR PRENTICE *hands him the boots.*
NICK *takes them into the dispensary.* SERGEANT MATCH
takes off his tunic and hands it to DR PRENTICE. NICK,
*without his shoes and wig, appears in the doorway of the dis-
pensary.* DR PRENTICE *hands him the* SERGEANT'*s tunic.*
NICK *turns.* DR PRENTICE *unzips his dress.* NICK *takes the
tunic into the dispensary.* SERGEANT MATCH *takes off his
shirt and tie.* NICK *wearing only his underpants, appears in the
doorway of the dispensary.* DR PRENTICE *hands him the*
SERGEANT'*s shirt and tie.* NICK *goes into the dispensary.*
SERGEANT MATCH *drops his trousers.* MRS PRENTICE *enters
from the hall. Seeing the* SERGEANT *without his trousers, she*

screams loudly. Shocked and embarrassed SERGEANT MATCH, *pulls up his trousers.*

MRS PRENTICE (*icily*). What were you doing with your trousers down, officer?

MATCH. The doctor is going to examine me.

MRS PRENTICE. Why?

MATCH. There's reason to suppose that I had a nasty experience a short time ago.

MRS PRENTICE. What kind of experience.

PRENTICE. He was meddled with.

MRS PRENTICE. By whom?

PRENTICE. Me.

MRS PRENTICE. And why are you examining him?

PRENTICE. To find out whether his story is true.

MRS PRENTICE. Don't you know?

PRENTICE. No. I didn't feel a thing.

MRS PRENTICE (*with a toss of her head*). Where is Dr Rance?

PRENTICE. He's just certified the hotel page. He's putting him in a padded cell.

MRS PRENTICE. I must speak to him. Things are getting out of control.

She hurries into the ward. DR PRENTICE *turns to* SERGEANT MATCH.

PRENTICE. Remove your trousers, sergeant, and we'll continue.

SERGEANT MATCH *takes off his trousers and hands them to* DR PRENTICE. *He is naked except for his underpants and socks. With a flourish* DR PRENTICE *takes the red pill-box from his pocket and hands it to the* SERGEANT.

(*Smiling.*) I'd like you to swallow these. Take as many as you like. They're quite harmless.

The SERGEANT *accepts the box.*

Now I want you to lie on this couch and concentrate on the closing chapters of your favourite work of fiction.

SERGEANT MATCH *lies on the couch.* DR PRENTICE *pulls the curtain around him and hurries to the dispensary with the trousers. He meets* NICK *in the doorway.* NICK *carries the* SERGEANT'*s uniform.* DR PRENTICE *hands him the trousers.*

(*To* NICK.) In the garden you'll find a little summer house. You won't be disturbed in there.

NICK *goes into the garden with the clothes.* DR PRENTICE *goes to the desk and pours a whisky. He swallows it quickly.* NICK *appears, without the uniform, in the french windows.*

NICK. The helmet, sir!

DR PRENTICE *hurries to the couch.*

PRENTICE. The helmet, sergeant!
MATCH (*from behind the curtain*). In the hall, sir.
PRENTICE (*to* NICK). Where are Miss Barclay's clothes?
NICK. In the dispensary!

NICK *hurries into the hall.* DR PRENTICE *hurries into the dispensary.* MRS PRENTICE *enters from the ward.* NICK *re-enters from the hall wearing only underpants and the helmet. Upon seeing him* MRS PRENTICE *shrieks and backs away.* NICK *runs into the garden.*

MRS PRENTICE (*at the desk, weakly*). Oh, this place is like a madhouse!

DR RANCE *enters from the ward.* MRS PRENTICE *turns upon him, wildly.*

You must help me, doctor! I keep seeing naked men.
RANCE (*pause*). When did these delusions start?
MRS PRENTICE. They're not delusions. They're real.
RANCE (*with a bray of laughter*). Everyone who suffers from hallucinations imagines they are real. When did you last think you saw a naked man?
MRS PRENTICE. Just now. He was nude except for a policeman's helmet.

RANCE (*drily*). It's not difficult to guess what's on your mind, my dear. Are you having marital troubles?

MRS PRENTICE. Well, I do suffer from neuritis. My husband refuses to prescribe anything.

RANCE. A man shouldn't have to drug his wife in order to achieve a happy union.

MRS PRENTICE. I don't want drugs. I want account taken of my sexual nature.

She goes to the desk and pours whisky. DR RANCE *speaks to her gently yet with firmness.*

RANCE. Your depraved appetites may have contributed in part to your husband's breakdown. Where is Dr Prentice?

MRS PRENTICE (*putting ice into her glass*). I don't know. When I returned from telephoning the Station Hotel he was undressing the sergeant.

RANCE. How would you describe his relations with the sergeant?

MRS PRENTICE. Strange and, in many ways, puzzling. He's called him into this room on several occasions and then abruptly dismissed him.

RANCE. Playing the coquette, eh? Well, well, it adds spice to a love affair. What news of the patient?

MRS PRENTICE. None. Except that this looks like the nightgown she was wearing. (*She holds up* GERALDINE'*s nightgown.*)

RANCE. She must be naked then?

MRS PRENTICE. Yes.

RANCE. And what's the report from the Station Hotel?

MRS PRENTICE. They state that they have no page called Gerald Barclay on their register. The youth you've certified insane must be an impostor.

RANCE. And what of Nicholas Beckett – the real page-boy?

MRS PRENTICE. He hasn't returned to the hotel. Yet when he disappeared his uniform was in my possession.

RANCE (*greatly concerned*). Two young people – one mad and

one sexually insatiable – both naked – are roaming this house. At all costs we must prevent a collision.

MRS PRENTICE. Oh, doctor! Does any of this make sense to you?

RANCE. It most certainly does. It's a human interest story. A respected member of the medical fraternity is married to a dazzlingly beautiful woman. Hopelessly in love but, through mutual distrust, refusing to admit it, there is little they can do to prevent a once-precious relationship turning sour. The doctor has a charming, but mentally unstable patient. She is the key to the mystery. At an early age she was the victim of a sexual attack. The assailant was her own father! An act of transference, common to the experience of any psychiatrist, allows her to identify the doctor as her parent. The demands of a nymphomaniac wife and patient, coupled with those of his torrid secretary, prove too much for his sanity. He turns, in his anguish, to assaulting young boys. Retaining, however, some vestiges of normal feelings, he persuades his minions to dress in women's clothes. This explains his desire for female garments. As his neurosis matures we'll better be able to decide whether he intended his boys to impersonate wife, patient or secretary.

MRS PRENTICE. And why did he assault the policeman?

RANCE. Pure madness. No other reason.

MRS PRENTICE. How long do you think my husband has been insane?

RANCE. I trace the origins of his illness as far back as that first letter to *The Guardian*. From the startling ideas of Dr Goebbels on the function of the male sexual organ we pass quite logically to white golliwogs. An attempt, in fact, to change the order of creation – homosexuality slots in here – dabbling in the black arts! The reported theft of the private parts of a well-known public figure ties in with this theory. We've phallic worship under our noses or I'm a Dutchman! (*With a neigh of laughter.*) When this is published I'll make my fortune. My 'documentary type' novelette will go into twelve record-breaking reprints. I'll be able to leave the service of the Commissioners and bask in the attentions of those who, like myself, find other people's iniquity puts money in their purse.

MRS PRENTICE (*drinking whisky with a shudder*). What a dreadful story. I'd condemn it in the strongest terms if it were fiction.

RANCE. I shan't now ask Dr Prentice to open our Mental Health Fair. (*Pressing his lips together.*) We'll have to fall back upon one of the saner members of the Cabinet.

MRS PRENTICE *picks a bright red pill-box from the floor near the couch.* DR RANCE *is quick to notice.*

What's that?

MRS PRENTICE. A pill-box, doctor. It's empty.

DR RANCE *seizes it and turns it over, with slowly growing horror.*

RANCE. He's taken an overdose! We have here terrible evidence of conflict. His tormented mind, seeking release, has led him to attempt to destroy himself.

MRS PRENTICE *gasps with shock and amazement.*

MRS PRENTICE. Suicide? This is so unexpected.

RANCE. Just when one least expects it, the unexpected always happens. We must find him before it's too late.

They part rapidly in opposite directions – MRS PRENTICE *into the hall,* DR RANCE *into the ward.* DR PRENTICE *and* NICK *enter simultaneously from the dispensary and the garden.* DR PRENTICE *carries the shoes and wig wrapped in the dress.* NICK *is wearing the* SERGEANT's *uniform.*

NICK (*urgent*). Miss Barclay is hanging from the window of the padded cell, doctor!

PRENTICE (*staring about the room*). Where can one hide a woman's dress in a doctor's consulting-room?

*He picks up the vase. It is now too small to contain the dress.
He looks around, quickly, desperate. The curtains of the couch
part and* SERGEANT MATCH *tumbles forward on to the floor,
drugged into insensibility.* DR PRENTICE *and* NICK *react to
the* SERGEANT'S *condition.* DR PRENTICE *feels in his pocket
and pulls out the square white pill-box. His eyes widen. He
clutches his throat.*

(*With a strangled cry.*) My God! I've poisoned him!

NICK *runs to the sink, wets a towel and flicks it into the*
SERGEANT'S *face.* DR PRENTICE *puts the dress down and
attempts to drag* SERGEANT MATCH *to his feet. The* SER-
GEANT *moans, stares about him in a stupor and shivers un-
controllably.*

NICK (*holding the* SERGEANT'S *pulse*). He's frozen, sir.
PRENTICE. The effect of the drug. We find the same process
at work in corpses.
NICK. Get some clothes on him and dump him outside. Let
him sleep it off.

He picks up the dress.

PRENTICE (*wringing his hands*). How shall I explain the
presence in my garden of the drugged body of a police
sergeant?
NICK (*putting the dress on to* SERGEANT MATCH). You're
guilty. You don't have to explain. Only the innocent do that.

He zips up the dress. DR PRENTICE *forces the* SERGEANT *to
his feet.*

PRENTICE (*with a wail*). Oh, if this gets out I'll be reduced to
selling matches!

They drag the semi-conscious SERGEANT MATCH *into the
garden.* MRS PRENTICE *enters from the hall,* DR RANCE *from
the ward.*

MRS PRENTICE. Someone has stolen the sergeant's helmet from the hall table. Do you suppose it could be my husband?

RANCE. Possibly. His behaviour is so ridiculous one might almost suspect him of being sane.

MRS PRENTICE, *at the french windows, suddenly cries out in alarm.*

What is it, my dear? You seem to express more emotion than is necessary at the mention of a policeman's helmet.

MRS PRENTICE. I've just seen my husband carrying a woman into the shrubbery.

RANCE. Was she struggling?

MRS PRENTICE. No.

RANCE. Then a new and frightening possibility presents itself. The drugs in this box – (*He lifts up the bright red pill-box.*) – may not have been used for suicide, but for murder. Your husband has made away with his secretary!

MRS PRENTICE *pours a whisky with a nervous laugh.*

MRS PRENTICE. Isn't that a little melodramatic, doctor?

RANCE. Lunatics *are* melodramatic. The subtleties of drama are wasted on them. The ugly shadow of anti-Christ stalks this house. Having discovered her Father/Lover in Dr Prentice the patient replaces him in a psychological re-shuffle by that archetypal Father-figure – the Devil himself. Everything is now clear. The final chapters of my book are knitting together: incest, buggery, outrageous women and strange love-cults catering for depraved appetites. All the fashionable bric-à-brac. A beautiful but neurotic girl has influenced the doctor to sacrifice a white virgin to propitiate the dark gods of unreason. 'When they broke into the evil-smelling den they found her poor body bleeding beneath the obscene and half-erect phallus.' (*To* MRS PRENTICE.) My 'unbiased account' of the case of the infamous sex-killer Prentice will undoubtedly add a great deal to our under-standing of such creatures. Society must be made aware of the growing menace of pornography. The whole treacherous avant-garde movement will be exposed for what it is – an instrument for inciting decent citizens to commit bizarre crimes against humanity and the state! (*He pauses, a little overcome and wipes his brow.*) You have, under your roof, my dear, one of the most remarkable lunatics of all time. We must institute a search for the corpse. As a transvestite, fetishist, bi-sexual murderer Dr Prentice displays considerable deviation overlap. We may get necrophilia too. As a sort of bonus.

DR PRENTICE *enters from the garden.*

(*Turning, and giving a disdainful stare.*) Would you confirm, Prentice, that your wife saw you carrying a body into the shrubbery?

PRENTICE. Yes. I have an explanation for my conduct.

RANCE. I'm not interested in your explanations. I can provide my own. Where is your secretary?

PRENTICE. I've given her the sack.

RANCE (*aside to* MRS PRENTICE). He killed her and wrapped her body in a sack. The word association is very clear.

PRENTICE. I haven't killed anyone!

RANCE. Your answer is in accord with the complex structure of your neurosis.

PRENTICE. The person my wife saw wasn't dead. They were asleep.

RANCE (*to* MRS PRENTICE). He hopes for a resurrection. We've a link here with primitive religion. (*To* DR PRENTICE.) Why have you turned your back on the God of your Fathers?

PRENTICE. I'm a rationalist.

RANCE. You can't be a rationalist in an irrational world. It isn't rational. (*Picking up the wig and shoes.*) Was it your intention to wear these for auto-erotic excitement?

PRENTICE. No, I'm a perfectly normal man.

RANCE (*to* MRS PRENTICE). His belief in normality is quite

abnormal. (*To* DR PRENTICE.) Was the girl killed before or after you took her clothes off?

PRENTICE. He wasn't a girl. He was a man.

MRS PRENTICE. He was wearing a dress.

PRENTICE. He was a man for all that.

RANCE. Women wear dresses, Prentice, not men. I won't be a party to the wanton destruction of a fine old tradition. Did you change clothes with your victim before it died?

PRENTICE. Nobody died! The person you saw me with was a policeman who'd taken an overdose of narcotics.

MRS PRENTICE. Why was he dressed as a woman?

PRENTICE. He was naked when I found him. The dress was readily to hand.

MRS PRENTICE. Where were his own clothes?

PRENTICE. A boy had stolen them.

DR RANCE *draws* MRS PRENTICE *aside, his face a mask of disapproval.*

RANCE. The time has come to call a halt to this Graeco-Roman hallucination. Is there a strait-jacket in the house?

MRS PRENTICE. Modern methods of treatment have rendered the strait-jacket obsolete.

RANCE. I'm well aware of that. We still use them none the less. Have you one in your possession?

MRS PRENTICE. The porter has a few.

RANCE. We can take no chances with your husband in his present condition.

He goes into the hall. DR PRENTICE, *at the desk, pouring whisky, spits his words venomously at his wife.*

PRENTICE. Is this another of your plots to undermine my reputation for sound judgement, you treacherous harpy?

MRS PRENTICE *makes no effort to reply. She smiles and puts a hand upon* DR PRENTICE's *shoulder.*

MRS PRENTICE (*gently*). You've caused a poor girl's death,

darling. You may be called upon to accept a period of restraint.

PRENTICE (*swallowing whisky*). Miss Barclay isn't dead!

MRS PRENTICE. Produce her then and your difficulties will be over.

PRENTICE. I can't.

MRS PRENTICE. Why not?

PRENTICE. You're wearing her dress. (*With a shrug of resignation.*) You surprised me this morning making an ill-timed attempt to seduce her.

MRS PRENTICE *smiles a smile of quiet disbelief.*

MRS PRENTICE. If we're to save our marriage, my dear, you must admit that you prefer boys to women. Dr Rance has explained the reasons for your aberration. You'll find me quite tolerant. In fact I know a number of charming youths. I could pass a few of the younger ones on to you. It would raise the tone of our marriage considerably.

DR PRENTICE *is stunned by her suggestion. He rounds on her in a fury.*

PRENTICE. I won't have you making scandalous allegations in a matter of which you know nothing.

MRS PRENTICE (*tossing her head*). The page at the hotel accused you of behaving in an indecent manner.

PRENTICE. That wasn't a boy. It was a girl.

MRS PRENTICE. Admit that you prefer your sex to mine. I've no hesitation in saying that I do.

PRENTICE. You filthy degenerate! Take your clothes off!

MRS PRENTICE *unzips her dress.*

MRS PRENTICE (*eagerly*). Are you going to beat me? Do if you wish. Your psychotic experiences are immensely valuable to you and should be encouraged rather than thwarted or repressed.

DR PRENTICE *seizes her, smacks her face and tears the dress from her. She struggles.*

MRS PRENTICE (*gasping as he slaps her*). Oh, my darling! This is the way to sexual adjustment in marriage.

DR PRENTICE *throws her from him. She crashes into the vase which topples to the floor.* DR RANCE *runs in from the hall with two strait-jackets.* DR PRENTICE *runs into the garden with his wife's dress.* MRS PRENTICE *sits among the overthrown flowers, her hair tousled, wearing only her underclothes.*

MRS PRENTICE (*rising, stumbling to the desk*). Oh, doctor, during your absence my husband became violent and struck me. (*She pours a whisky.*)

RANCE. Did you enjoy it?

MRS PRENTICE. At first. But the pleasures of the senses quickly pall.

She drinks the whisky. DR RANCE *stoops and picks up the vase and scattered flowers.*

RANCE. Was there an attempt to destroy these flowers?

MRS PRENTICE. They fell during the struggle.

RANCE. You're aware of the plant allegory? The rose is a common cipher for a woman. He intended to do you harm.

MRS PRENTICE. Yes. I was beaten until I was nearly senseless.

RANCE. Oh, that was a mere physical act with no special psychological significance. We must lose no time in putting Dr Prentice under restraint. We'll need help in the enterprise. Have you no brawny youth upon whom you can call in times of stress?

MRS PRENTICE. I'm a married woman, doctor! Your suggestion is in the worst of taste.

NICK *enters from the garden dressed in the* SERGEANT'S *uniform.*

NICK. I'd like a word with you, doctor, about my brother, Nicholas Beckett. I've just arrested him.

RANCE. Such a touching demonstration of brotherly love is quite in key with the spirit of the age. Why did you arrest him?

NICK. He'd broken the law.

RANCE. And because of that he's to be treated as a criminal? What's happened to the British love of fair play? Where is your brother now?

NICK. In gaol.

RANCE (*to* MRS PRENTICE). Your sleep won't be disturbed tonight, my dear.

MRS PRENTICE. Life is full of disappointments.

RANCE (*to* NICK). Where is Sergeant Match?

NICK. Keeping my brother company.

RANCE. Has he been charged?

NICK. He hasn't committed a crime.

RANCE (*to* MRS PRENTICE). When the punishment for guilt or innocence is the same it becomes an act of logic to commit the crime. (*To* NICK.) Was Dr Prentice in the garden?

NICK. No.

RANCE. You may have difficulty in recognizing him. He was probably dressed as a woman.

MRS PRENTICE. He has killed his secretary.

NICK (*horrified*). He can't've done. He's an O.B.E.

RANCE. These cabbalistic signs are of no more use in warding off evil than the moons and stars on a sorcerer's hat. We shall need your help in tracking down the mindless killer of young Geraldine Barclay.

NICK *stares at* DR RANCE.

NICK (*with a groan*). Oh, doctor, I'm obsessed by feelings of guilt. I have to make a confession.

RANCE. You must ring for an appointment. I can't listen to confessions off the cuff.

NICK. I am Nicholas Beckett. I've no right to wear this uniform. (*He takes off his helmet.*) I did it at the doctor's request never imagining that I was unwittingly assisting a psychopath.

RANCE. You have no brother? And Sergeant Match isn't in custody?

NICK. No. I'm a page-boy employed by the Station Hotel. I met Dr Prentice quite by chance. I took to him instantly. After a short conversation during which we discussed sex matters in an uninhibited and free-wheeling way, he asked me if I'd mind dressing up as a woman. I agreed to his suggestion having heard that transvestism is no longer held to be a dangerous debilitating vice. The doctor introduced me to his colleagues as 'Miss Barclay'. I was to be paid a sum of money. (*To* MRS PRENTICE.) That's why I objected to being undressed. It would've embarrassed me.

MRS PRENTICE (*to* DR RANCE). You understand what this means, doctor?

RANCE. Yes. Miss Barclay has been missing since this morning. (*To* NICK.) When Dr Prentice asked you to pose as a woman did he give a reason?

NICK. No.

MRS PRENTICE. Didn't you consider his request strange?

NICK. No.

RANCE. Have you aided other men in their perverted follies?

NICK. During my last term at school I was the slave of a corporal in the Welsh Fusiliers.

RANCE. Were you never warned of the dangers inherent in such relationships?

NICK. When he was posted abroad he gave me a copy of 'The Way to Healthy Manhood'.

RANCE (*drily, to* MRS PRENTICE). A case of opening the stable door after the horse is in. (*To* NICK.) Your life appears to have been spent among the more brutal and irresponsible members of society. You'd better help me to right the wrongs you've done.

NICK. What do you want me to do, sir? After my recent experiences I'm understandably suspicious.

RANCE. You'll find the demands of medicine easier to satisfy than those of the army. (*He picks up the strait-jacket.*) This is a strait-jacket. I require your help in persuading Dr Prentice to put it on. There may be violence. His body has a mind of its own. (*To* MRS PRENTICE.) Have you a gun?

MRS PRENTICE opens a drawer in the desk and takes out two guns.

MRS PRENTICE (*handing one to* DR RANCE). You will make sure before you fire that my husband isn't waving an olive branch?

RANCE. An olive branch can be used as an offensive weapon. If there's trouble I shall blow him from the floor.

NICK (*to* DR RANCE). You're going to flush him from his hiding-place, sir?

RANCE. Yes. Really we should hire beaters, but they'll expect to have their fares paid from Scotland. (*He goes to the french windows, shaking his head.*) I'm loath to certify a fellow psychiatrist. It causes such bad feelings within the profession.

He goes into the garden.

MRS PRENTICE (*to* NICK). Take no chances. Call for help immediately you see Dr Prentice. (*She goes to the hall door, waving the gun.*) Try not to break his arms or legs. It makes the job of adjusting the jacket doubly difficult.

She goes into the hall. NICK *opens the strait-jacket.* DR PRENTICE *enters from the ward carrying the dress taken from* MRS PRENTICE. *He looks harassed.*

PRENTICE. Miss Barclay has fallen from the window of the padded cell. When I asked her to undress she became hysterical.

NICK *nods, understandingly. He walks across to* DR PRENTICE *and takes him firmly by the shoulder.*

NICK. Come along now, doctor, I want you to put this on. (*He lifts the jacket.*)

PRENTICE (*hardly hearing*). I want you to co-operate with me in getting things back to normal in this house.

NICK (*soothingly*). You can rely on me, sir.

PRENTICE. It would help me considerably if you'd take your clothes off.

NICK (*pause*). If I do that, sir, will you put this on? (*He holds up the jacket.*)

PRENTICE (*angry, losing patience*). Of course not! That's a strait-jacket. I won't be a party to kinky capers. You've lived too long at the Station Hotel to know how decent people behave. Now do as I say and undress!

SERGEANT MATCH, *wearing the leopard-spotted dress appears in the french windows.*

MATCH (*swaying, unsteadily*). I'm ready to be examined when you are, doctor.

He stumbles into the dispensary, clutching the furniture, his face pale, his eyes staring. GERALDINE, *wearing* NICK's *uniform, staggers in from the garden. Her face is bruised and smeared with soil. She is white with shock.*

GERALDINE. They're combing the grounds for us, doctor! They've got guns. What shall we do?

PRENTICE. You must lose no time in getting undressed. (*He seizes her and attempts to unbutton her uniform.*)

GERALDINE (*tearful, beating him away*). You're behaving like a maniac!

NICK. He is a maniac. He's murdered a woman and hidden her body somewhere.

PRENTICE. Who is responsible for these vile stories?

NICK. Dr Rance is having you certified. (*Waving the jacket.*) I've got to get you into this!

He leaps upon DR PRENTICE *and attempts to put him into the strait-jacket.* DR PRENTICE *pulls* GERALDINE's *trousers down. She beats him away, weeping profusely. She pulls her trousers up.* DR PRENTICE *wards off* NICK *and tries to prevent* GERALDINE *pulling up her trousers.* SERGEANT MATCH *enters dizzily from the dispensary, stumbling across the room, crashing and upsetting furniture.*

MATCH. I'm ready when you are, doctor!

He reels out into the ward. DR PRENTICE *shakes* NICK *away, furiously.*

PRENTICE (*to* GERALDINE). Give this youth the clothes you're wearing. (*He lifts the dress.*) Put this on. (*To* NICK.) Let the sergeant have his uniform back. When he next passes through we can confiscate my wife's dress and our problems will be solved.

NICK *takes off his uniform.* GERALDINE *pulls down her trousers. A shot is heard from the ward.* SERGEANT MATCH *enters. Blood is pouring down his leg.*

MATCH. I was on the lavatory, doctor, when a man appeared and fired a gun at me. I'd like your opinion as to the extent of the damage.

He reels into the dispensary. A crash is heard. NICK *is now naked except for his underpants.* MRS PRENTICE *enters from the hall.* NICK *ducks behind the desk,* GERALDINE *is concealed from view by the couch.* MRS PRENTICE *advances on* DR PRENTICE.

MRS PRENTICE (*waving the gun*). Come with me and lie down!
PRENTICE. The woman is insatiable.
MRS PRENTICE. Unless you make love to me I shall shoot you.
PRENTICE. No husband can be expected to give his best at gun-point. (*Backing away.*)

MRS PRENTICE *fires.* DR PRENTICE *ducks and runs quickly from the room into the garden.* MRS PRENTICE *follows and fires again.* SERGEANT MATCH *runs out of the dispensary,*

terrified. Seeing him MRS PRENTICE *screams.* SERGEANT
MATCH *gives a bellow of fright and runs into the hall.* NICK
runs from behind the desk into the hall. MRS PRENTICE *squeals
with surprise.* GERALDINE, *wearing the top half of* NICK's
uniform and no trousers, runs into the dispensary. MRS PREN-
TICE *runs to the ward door. As she reaches it a shot is heard
and* NICK *re-enters, moaning and clutching his shoulder.
Screaming with terror* MRS PRENTICE *fires wildly at* NICK
who gives a yelp of pain and runs into the garden. DR RANCE
enters from the ward holding a smoking gun. MRS PRENTICE
flings herself upon him.

MRS PRENTICE. Doctor, doctor! The world is full of naked
men running in all directions!

DR RANCE *grabs her arm.*

RANCE. Where do you keep your tranquillizers?

MRS PRENTICE *hurries into the dispensary. A cry and a
crash are heard and* GERALDINE *runs out. She has taken off
the uniform and wears her own panties and bra.*

RANCE (*with a bray of triumph*). At last we've caught the
patient!

He points his gun at GERALDINE. MRS PRENTICE *runs from
the dispensary with a strait-jacket and flings it over* GERAL-
DINE.

GERALDINE. I'm not a patient. I'm telling the truth!
RANCE. It's much too late to tell the truth.

*They drag the weeping girl to the couch and fasten her into the
strait-jacket.*

RANCE (*watching as* MRS PRENTICE *ties* GERALDINE *down*).
These final harrowing scenes will be lavishly illustrated with
graphs showing the effect of her downfall upon her poor
tortured mind. Meanwhile, in his temple of love, the hideous

Dr Prentice and his acolyte are praying to their false gods unaware that the forces of reason have got their measure.

MRS PRENTICE *steps back.*

Fetch a syringe.

MRS PRENTICE *goes into the dispensary.*

GERALDINE (*trussed up, unable to move*). What have I done to deserve this? I've always led such a respectable life.

RANCE. Your mind has given way. You'll find the experience invaluable in your efforts to come to terms with twentieth-century living. Why did you persuade your father to kill Geraldine Barclay?

GERALDINE. I am Geraldine Barclay.

RANCE. You imagine you're a secretary. In fact you're the leading player in one of the most remarkable and sinister stories of recent history. The extent to which you influenced your employer and contributed to his breakdown has yet to be measured.

GERALDINE (*weeping, bitterly*). This is dreadful. Dreadful.

RANCE. I'm glad you're adopting a more responsible attitude. It's most encouraging. Where is the body?

GERALDINE. I don't know.

RANCE. Are you under the seal of the confessional? What black rites were you initiated into by that foul priest of the Unknown?

GERALDINE *sobs, unable to speak.* DR RANCE *abruptly throws himself on to her and holds her in his arms.*

Let me cure your neurosis! It's the only thing I want out of life.

MRS PRENTICE *enters from the dispensary carrying a hypodermic syringe and bowl.*

MRS PRENTICE. What is the meaning of this exhibition?

RANCE (*breaking away from* GERALDINE). It's a new and

hitherto untried type of therapy. I think it's viable under the circumstances.

MRS PRENTICE. Your treatment seems designed to plunge the patient deeper into lunacy rather than achieve any lasting cure.

DR RANCE *rounds on her with icy dignity.*

RANCE. Someone whose unconscious is as quirky as your own could hardly be expected to understand my methods.

MRS PRENTICE. What do you mean by that?

RANCE. I'm referring to those manifestations of the penis which you encounter with an increasing degree of frequency.

MRS PRENTICE. You've seen them too.

RANCE. What does that prove? Merely that you've given me your wretched disease. (*He takes the hypodermic from her.*)

MRS PRENTICE. Shall I swab the patient's arm?

RANCE. You don't imagine I'm wasting this stuff on her, do you? (*He rolls back his sleeve.*) At five guineas an ounce it would be criminal. (*He gives himself an injection.*) Go and call the police.

MRS PRENTICE *goes into the hall.* DR RANCE *puts the hypodermic aside.* MRS PRENTICE *re-enters, wild-eyed, her hands smeared with blood.*

MRS PRENTICE. There's a policeman outside. Naked and covered in blood.

RANCE. The bounds of decency have long been overstepped in this house. (*He slaps her face.*) Your subconscious cannot be encouraged in its skulduggery.

MRS PRENTICE (*desperate, showing her hands*). Is this blood real?

RANCE. No.

MRS PRENTICE. Can you see it?

RANCE. Yes.

MRS PRENTICE. Then what explanation is there?

RANCE. I'm a scientist. I state facts, I cannot be expected to

provide explanations. Reject any para-normal phenomena.
It's the only way to remain sane.

MRS PRENTICE. It seems real.

RANCE. Who are you to decide what reality is? Remain where
you are. I'll call the police.

He goes into the hall. MRS PRENTICE *pours herself a whisky.*
NICK *appears in the french windows, pale, swaying unsteadily
and bleeding from a wound on his shoulder. Blood oozes from
between his fingers.*

NICK (*anguished, fainting*). I'm in pain. I've been shot. Call a
doctor.

MRS PRENTICE (*dropping her glass, hiding her head in her hands*).
Oh, I'm losing my mind!

She sobs to herself. GERALDINE *calls to* NICK.

GERALDINE. Help me! I'm suffering untold anguish. Untie
me.

NICK. Why are you tied up?

GERALDINE. Dr Rance did it. He says I'm mad.

NICK. He's a psychiatrist, he must know. He wouldn't put you
in a strait-jacket if you were sane. He'd have to be mad.

GERALDINE. He is mad!

NICK *supports himself on the desk and stares at the sobbing*
MRS PRENTICE.

NICK (*to* GERALDINE). Is she mad?

GERALDINE. She thinks she is. She imagines you're a figment
of her imagination.

NICK (*to* MRS PRENTICE, *nodding to* GERALDINE). She can
see me. Doesn't that prove I'm real?

MRS PRENTICE. No. She's mad.

NICK. If you think I'm a phantom of your subconscious you
must be mad.

MRS PRENTICE (*with a hysterical shriek*). I am mad!

GERALDINE *bursts into tears.* NICK *hangs over the desk, blood pouring from his wound.* DR PRENTICE *hurries in from the garden.*

PRENTICE. My wife has shot at me. She thinks I'm mad!

NICK. You are mad! I've been told to put you into a strait-jacket.

He picks MRS PRENTICE'S *gun from the desk, lifts the strait-jacket and advances on* DR PRENTICE. MRS PRENTICE *covers her face with her hands.* DR RANCE *runs in from the hall carrying another strait-jacket. He flings it over* MRS PRENTICE. *They crash to the floor screaming and struggling.*

PRENTICE (*to* NICK). Put that gun down! (*To* DR RANCE.) A husband must be allowed to put his wife into a strait-jacket. It's one of the few pleasures left in modern marriage.

He makes a move. NICK *holds out the jacket with one hand and waves the gun with the other.*

You should have that wound attended to. Have you a handkerchief?

NICK. No.

PRENTICE. Borrow mine.

He pulls his handkerchief from his pocket. It is full of flower stalks. He tosses them into NICK'S *face.* NICK *is knocked off guard.* DR PRENTICE *flings himself on to him. They join* DR RANCE *and* MRS PRENTICE *in a struggling, grunting heap on the floor watched by the tearful* GERALDINE *from the couch.* DR PRENTICE *wrenches the gun from* NICK *and stands.* NICK *moans and crawls away, his wound streaming blood, his face white and ill.* DR RANCE *stands to his feet having tied* MRS PRENTICE *into a strait-jacket.*

PRENTICE (*waving his gun*). Stay where you are, doctor! Your conduct today has been a model of official irresponsibility and bloody-mindedness. I'm going to certify you.

RANCE (*quietly, with dignity*). No. I am going to certify you.

PRENTICE. I have the weapon. You have the choice. What is it to be? Either madness or death?

RANCE. Neither of your alternatives would enable me to continue to be employed by Her Majesty's Government.

PRENTICE. That isn't true. The higher reaches of the civil service are recruited entirely from corpses or madmen. Press the alarm!

DR RANCE *goes to the wall and presses the alarm. A siren wails. Metal grilles fall over each of the doors. The lights go out. The siren wails to a stop. The room is lit only by the glare of a bloody sunset shining through the trees in the garden.*

An overloading of the circuit! We're trapped.

RANCE (*drily*). I hope the security arrangements in the wards are as efficient as those in your consulting-room. We could starve to death.

PRENTICE. A fitting tribute to the effectiveness of our early warning system.

RANCE. Since neither of us can escape your deterrent is useless. Put it down.

DR PRENTICE *puts the gun on to the desk.* DR RANCE *takes out his own and points it at the astonished* DR PRENTICE.

RANCE (*holding* DR PRENTICE *at bay with one gun and picking up the other*). I'll have you in a jacket within the hour. It's a hat trick!

PRENTICE. Is this a record for you?

RANCE (*slipping* DR PRENTICE's *gun into his pocket*). By no means. I once put a whole family into a communal straitjacket.

PRENTICE. How proud your mother must've been.

RANCE. She wasn't, I'm afraid. It was my own family, you see. I've a picture of the scene at home. My foot placed squarely upon my father's head. I sent it to Sigmund Freud and had a charming postcard in reply.

NICK *crawls, almost fainting, to a chair.*

NICK. What about me, sir? I'm not mad.

RANCE (*with a smile*). You're not human.

NICK. I can't be an hallucination. (*He points to his bleeding shoulder.*) Look at this wound. That's real.

RANCE. It appears to be.

NICK. If the pain is real I must be real.

RANCE. I'd rather not get involved in metaphysical speculation.

PRENTICE. This young man is the page-boy from the Station Hotel. He misbehaved himself with my wife. He wasn't an hallucination when he did that.

RANCE. Your wife is subject to a type of nervous disorder which leads her to imagine she is being pursued by unclothed male figures. This young man is one of them. If he is her assailant it follows that the assault was a fabrication of her diseased mind.

PRENTICE. But Sergeant Match wishes to arrest the young man.

RANCE. The sergeant too may not exist. According to your wife he also appeared to her naked. For all we know he could be a type of incubus employed by Scotland Yard. He admitted that his brother was a figment of his imagination confirming my own law that the relations of apparitions are also apparitions. (*In a firm voice.*) What have you done with Geraldine Barclay?

GERALDINE (*feebly*). I'm here.

DR PRENTICE *goes to the desk and pours a large whisky.*

PRENTICE (*to* DR RANCE). The story you're about to hear is concerned solely with the heart: the mind and its mysteries could not have been further from my thoughts when, early this morning, I persuaded that young woman to take her clothes off. (*He drinks the whisky.*)

GERALDINE (*to* DR RANCE). Mrs Prentice mistook my dress for her own and, by an oversight, you mistook me for a patient. Dr Prentice asked me to keep quiet in order to protect his good name. What could I do? I was terrified of exposure.

RANCE. You were naked at the time?

GERALDINE. Yes. Under duress I agreed to help the doctor. I've never ceased reproaching myself. The whole day has been spent fighting to retain my self-respect.

DR RANCE *chews his lip and turns abruptly to* DR PRENTICE.

RANCE. Release her. And your wife. (*As* DR PRENTICE *does so he stares, baffled.*) I'd be willing to stake my professional reputation upon the fact that this girl has been the victim of an incestuous attack. I won't go back upon my diagnosis. My publishers will sue me for loss of royalties.

GERALDINE (*stepping from the couch*). I'm sure my typing speed has been affected by what I've suffered today. (*Tearful, to* DR PRENTICE.) And I wish to report the loss of my lucky elephant charm.

DR RANCE *takes a brooch from his pocket.*

RANCE. Is this the piece of jewellery to which you refer?

GERALDINE. Yes. It has great sentimental value.

DR RANCE *gives it to her.* NICK *picks up the trousers of his uniform.*

NICK. I've got a brooch like that. (*He shows* GERALDINE *a brooch.*) You see – they make a pair!

MRS PRENTICE, *released now from the strait-jacket, gives a cry of surprise.*

MRS PRENTICE. Let me see those pieces of jewellery. (*The two brooches are shown to her.*) A single brooch can be made of these two fragments. (*She fits the brooch together.*) Oh, my heart is beating like a wild thing!

DR RANCE *examines the brooch.*

RANCE. Two elephants carrying a richly engraved howdah in

which is seated a young and beautiful woman – perhaps a princess of the royal line – magnificent example of oriental craftsmanship. (*To* MRS PRENTICE.) How did you know this was a single piece?

MRS PRENTICE. It belonged to me once. Many years ago, when I was a young woman, I was raped in a linen cupboard on the second floor of the Station Hotel. As the man left me he pressed that brooch into my hands in part payment.

RANCE. How did these children come to be in possession of the separate halves?

MRS PRENTICE. I paid for my misdemeanour by conceiving twins. It was impossible for me to keep them – I was by then engaged to be married to a promising young psychiatrist. I decided to abandon them to their fate. I broke the brooch in half and pinned a separate piece to each babe. I then placed them at either end of the small country town in which I was resident. Some kind people must've brought the children up as their own. (*Weeping, hugging* NICK *and* GERALDINE.) Oh, children! I am your mother! Can you ever forgive me for what I did?

NICK. What kind of mother must you have been to stay alone at the Station Hotel?

MRS PRENTICE. I was employed as a chambermaid. I did it for a joke shortly after the war. The effect of a Labour Government on the middle-classes had to be seen to be believed.

GERALDINE. Was our father also employed by the Station Hotel?

MRS PRENTICE. I never saw your father. The incident occurred during a power-cut. I became pregnant as I waited for normal services to be resumed.

DR PRENTICE, *his face white with shock, comes forward.*

PRENTICE (*weakly, to* DR RANCE). You'll find an inscription on the back of the brooch, sir –

DR RANCE *turns the brooch over.*

PRENTICE.—'To Lillian from Avis. Christmas 1939'. I found that brooch many years ago. It was on the pavement outside a large department store.

RANCE. Who were Lillian and Avis?

PRENTICE. I've no idea. It fell from the collar of a pekinese. Lillian and Avis may have been the creature's owners. (*He stares about him in shame.*) I haven't seen it since I pressed it into the hand of a chambermaid whom I debauched shortly before my marriage.

MRS PRENTICE (*with a cry of recognition*). I understand now why you suggested that we spend our wedding night in a linen cupboard!

PRENTICE. I wished to recreate a moment that was very precious to me. If you'd given in to my request our marriage would never have foundered.

MRS PRENTICE. From this time on we'll never make love except in a linen cupboard. It's the least I can do after the years of suffering I've caused you!

He embraces her and embraces NICK *and* GERALDINE.

RANCE (*to* PRENTICE, *wild with delight*). If you are this child's father my book can be written in good faith – she *is* the victim of an incestuous assault!

MRS PRENTICE. And so am I, doctor! My son has a collection of indecent photographs which prove beyond doubt that he made free with me in the same hotel – indeed in the same linen cupboard where his conception took place.

RANCE. Oh, what joy this discovery gives me! (*Embracing* MRS PRENTICE, GERALDINE *and* NICK.) Double incest is even more likely to produce a best-seller than murder – and this is as it should be for love *must* bring greater joy than violence.

Everyone embraces one another. The skylight opens, a rope ladder is lowered and, in a great blaze of glory, SERGEANT MATCH, *the leopard-spotted dress torn from one shoulder and streaming with blood, descends.*

We're approaching what our racier novelists term 'the climax'.

Reaching the floor SERGEANT MATCH *stares about him in bewilderment.*

MATCH. Will someone produce or cause to be produced the missing parts of Sir Winston Churchill?

RANCE. We have no knowledge of such things.

MATCH. I must ask for your co-operation in a matter of vital importance to this country. (*He sways, but hangs on to the rope ladder.*) Who was the last to see Mrs Barclay dead?

GERALDINE. The undertaker.

MATCH. Did he have no words of comfort for you as the only living descendant of a woman violated by the hero of 1940?

GERALDINE. He handed me a box.

MATCH. What did it contain?

GERALDINE. I assumed it held the clothes my step-mother wore on the day of her death. I was going to deliver them to some poor and needy person.

MATCH. Where is the box?

GERALDINE *picks up the box which she had upon entering the room. It has remained on the desk ever since.* SERGEANT MATCH *opens the box, looks inside, and gives a sigh.*

The Great Man can once more take up his place in the High Street as an example to us all of the spirit that won the Battle of Britain.

RANCE *looks inside the box.*

RANCE (*with admiration*). How much more inspiring if, in those dark days, we'd seen what we see now. Instead we had to be content with a cigar – the symbol falling far short, as we all realize, of the object itself.

GERALDINE *looks inside the box.*

GERALDINE. But it is a cigar!

RANCE. Ah, the illusions of youth!

SERGEANT MATCH *loudly shuts the lid of the box and tucks it under his arm.*

PRENTICE. Well, sergeant, we have been instrumental in uncovering a number of remarkable peccadilloes today. I'm sure you'll co-operate in keeping them out of the papers?

MATCH. I will, sir.

RANCE. I'm glad you don't despise tradition. Let us put our clothes on and face the world.

They pick up their clothes and weary, bleeding, drugged and drunk, climb the rope ladder into the blazing light.

Curtain